HI...
...OF GOATS
BY
ROBERT A. VANDERHOOF V.MD.

Christian Veterinary Mission
19303 Fremont Avenue North
Seattle, WA 98133 USA
Current Book Information at:
www.cvmusa.org
PHONE: (206) 546-7569 FAX: (206) 546-7458

Christian
Veterinary
Mission

THIS IS THE THIRD EDITION

It can be improved with your help. If you are a veterinary technician, small ruminant producer, animal husbandry worker, missionary, development worker or anyone with ideas or suggestions for ways this booklet could be changed to better meet the needs of your people, please write to the authors at Christian Veterinary Mission, 19303 FREMONT AVE. N., SEATTLE, WA 98133, PHONE: 206/546-7569; FAX 206/546-7458.

Thank you for your help.

Library of Congress Cataloging-in-Publication Data

Vanderhoof, Robert A.
  Raising healthy goats / by Robert A. Vanderhoof. — 3rd ed.
     p. cm.
  Includes bibliographical references.
  ISBN 1-886532-04-4 (pbk.)
  1. Goats. 2. Goats—Diseases. 3. Goats—Health. I. Christian Veterinary
Mission. II. Title.
SF383.V36 2006
636.3'9089—dc22

                                                                2006045437

ACKNOWLEDGEMENTS

I am indebted to my wife, Margaret, who encouraged me in the compiling of this book.

A special thanks to Diane Goldman of San Luis Obispo and Lisa Mates, Visalia, CA, for typing this manuscript, and to Cyndee Willis of Atascadero for help and advice in the preparation, and to Mr. Steve Taylor of Atascadero for his excellent illustrations all through the book.

Dr. M. A. Hammarlund is a veterinarian in Riverside, California, who has special interest in goats as a food animal, and is the author of "Raising Healthy Poultry under Primitive Conditions," one of the several books in the CVM series. He is a graduate of Kansas State University and did graduate study in animal pathology at Colorado State University. In addition to his practice, he has traveled to the Philippines, Bolivia and Costa Rica to assist in various programs. He carefully reviewed the final manuscript for which I owe him my gratitude.

A special recognition is due the publication, "Raising Goats for Milk and Meat," a Heifer Project International Training Course, third printing, July 1985, Rosalee Sinn.

I owe a debt of gratitude to Dr. Floyd Votaw of Fullerton, California, who with his wife spent several years in Haiti, assisting the people in that land with their problems of raising domestic animals and poultry, for his invaluable help and advice in formulating Section XXI. He supplied information particularly on the Leucena plant and the special soil condition known as laterite found in many parts of the world, but especially in Haiti and the Philippines.

This second edition, which is a thorough revision, would not have been possible without the efficiency and advice of Claudette Hall of Weaverville, California. She spent many hours in feeding information into her computer.

Mr. Harold McMahon of Woodlake, California is to be also commended for a number of excellent line drawings.

Special recognition is very much in order to Mrs. Charlie (Judy) Mills of Woodlake for her many outstanding illustrations throughout this publication.

So, my heart felt gratitude is extended to the above friends who without their help, this book would not have been produced.

The author's 7 year old granddaughter, Victoria Ashley Vanderhoof, with baby goat.

FOREWORD

The author's sincere desire in preparing this booklet is that it will serve to be readily used as a reference and aid in the raising of goats. Veterinary information and assistance are in short supply or nonexistent in many areas of the world. The author has endeavored to write this booklet in a brief style, touching on the most important diseases and conditions and providing appropriate dosages, treatments and recommendations. Much of the contents was borrowed from a larger and more technical compendium of 350 pages entitled "Health Care of the Goat and Sheep", 1987 by R.A. Vanderhoof VMD.

The writer of this booklet has been in veterinary practice for 46 years, taking care of both large and small animals. After graduating from the University of Pennsylvania, School of Veterinary Medicine, he was intimately associated with his father introducing and developing the Polled Hereford breed of beef cattle in California. His 6000 acre cattle ranch was located at Woodlake, California in the foothills of the High Sierra range of mountains.

The author has traveled to Haiti, helping with veterinary work, as well as Mexico and Bolivia and to Havasupai Indians down in the Grand Canyon of Arizona. He also made a trip to Israel in 1968.

He has been in active veterinary practice in Central California as well as in the Mojave Desert and the Coastal areas of San Luis Obispo County. Much of his time was spent on working with small ruminants (sheep and goats).

Robert A. Vanderhoof, V.M.D.
880 No. Valencia
Woodlake, CA 93286
May 15, 1994

NOTE: Dr. Robert Vanderhoof is deceased. Slight revisions have been made by Dr. Ivan Barineau and Dr. Keith Flanagan who are working in Haiti with Christian Veterinary Mission and Dr. Richard Stobaeus of Brunswick, GA.

Raising Healthy Animal Series

Christian Veterinary Mission (CVM), in its efforts to be meaningfully involved in Third World development work, quickly found there was little appropriate educational material available. CVM set about developing basic resource materials in animal husbandry for farmers and agricultural workers. Apparently, they met a real need, as these books have been accepted throughout the developing nations of the world.

The series of books published by Christian Veterinary Mission includes the following in order of publication:

Raising Healthy Pigs	Drugs and Their Usage
Raising Healthy Rabbits	Where There Is No Animal Doctor
Raising Healthy Fish	Raising Healthy Horses
Raising Healthy Cattle	Zoonoses
Raising Healthy Poultry	Raising Healthy Honey Bees
Raising Healthy Goats	Slaughter and Preservation of Meat
Raising Healthy Sheep	

As supplies are exhausted, they are revised before being republished in order to insure that they are kept current without compromising their simple, easy to read, well-illustrated style. All are in English, but it is our intention to publish these in other languages as soon as they are translated and funds become available for printing. The Pig, Poultry, Rabbit and Goat Books have been translated and printed in Spanish. The Poultry Book has been translated and printed in French. We hope to develop one on Camels and Buffalo.

CVM fieldworkers have also developed specific training materials for the countries in which they work.

All of these books have been put together by Christian men and women; in a labor of love and service, for people in need throughout the world. It demonstrates dedication to their profession, service to humanity and a witness to their faith. We hope that they are a help to you in developing an appropriate livestock program to meet your needs. We pray God's blessings on their use.

They may be ordered by e-mail:

bfrye@cvmusa.org or by phone, 206-546-7248.

Leroy Dorminy
Founder, CVM E-Mail missionvet@aol.com

TABLE OF CONTENTS

9

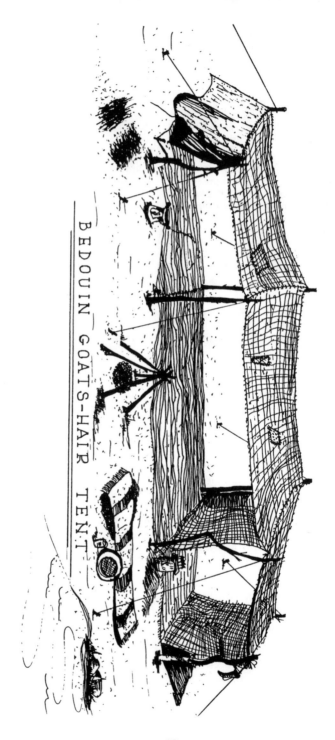

BEDOUIN GOATS-HAIR TENT

Section 1

Overview of General Information

1. OVERVIEW OF GENERAL INFORMATION[1]

Goats were among the earliest animals to be domesticated. Most countries of the world have used goats as a source of meat and milk since the earliest days of recorded history.

Goats play a positive role in environmental protection and destruction by clearing away certain plant species. The dairy goat is an ideal family dairy animal. It is friendly, alert, intelligent, socially inclined and manageable.

Goat populations are large in mountainous areas where they thrive on grass and browse (brush). This animal is very valuable to people in small, hilly, dry countries.

As well as having an important role in agriculture, goats can contribute significantly in improving the health of humans, e.g., the infant suffering from allergy to mother's or cow's milk, and raise the standard of living as well as the economy.

GOAT PRODUCTS

The most important goat products are milk, cheese, butter, meat, mohair and leather. Meat from goats is called chevon. Usually wethers (castrated males) are used for meat about weaning time.

TERMINOLOGY

Caprine - Latin designation for goats.
Buck - male goat
Wether - a castrated male
Doe - (pronounced dōh) female goat
Buckling - young male
Doeling - young female
Kid - young goat
Kidding - birthing process

BREEDS

Table 1. Some Important Breeds and Types of Goats.[2]

Breed	Origin	Breed	Origin
Dairy Type		**Milk and Meat Type**	
Alpine	Europe	Barbari	India, Pakistan
Anglo-Nubian	England, Sudan India	Damadcus	Syria
La Mancha	U.S.A, Spain	Jamnapari	India, Pakistan
Toggenburg	Europe	Nubian	Sudan
Saanen	Europe		
Oberhasli	Europe		
		Fiber	
		Angora	Turkey, S Africa Texas
		Cashmere	Iran, China

BREEDS

Table 1. Some Important Breeds and Types of Goats.[2]

Breed	Origin	Breed	Origin
Meat Type			
Boer	S. Africa		
Ma Tou	China		
Kambing Kajang	Malaysia	**Skins**	
Sapel	N. Africa	Mubende	Uganda
Pygmy	W. Africa	Red Sokoto	W. Africa

As to breeds of dairy goats, the most prominent in America and Europe are:

Nubians - originate from the Near East and have large pendulant ears and slightly Roman noses. They produce milk with the highest butterfat, about 4 to 5%. They come in various colors and patterns.

Alpine - are from the French-Swiss area. They have upright ears and come in various colors.

Oberhaslie - are bred from the Alpines and are solid brown.

Saanen - are the largest bodied of the breeds and are nearly all white. They produce the most milk, with probably the lowest butterfat content, about 3%. They have upright ears.

Toggenburg - a Swiss breed with distinct and constant markings of gray and white. They have upright ears.

La Mancha - originated in Spain. Their outstanding feature is a real short, or no ears. This breed comes in various colors and patterns. They are vey docile and loveable animals and are good milkers.

Angora - are not classed as a dairy or meat producing goat, but are raised for their distinctive mohair. They are white, have upright ears, and their horns are left intact. They are smaller in size.

Cashmere - known for long, fine fiber coats.

Boer - a meat goat that was developed in S. Africa. It has a large frame with a well developed muscling. Mature bucks may weigh up to 145 kg. with does weighing up to 90 kg. The boer goat is very docile and placid with an excellent temperament. It has a white body and a brown head with a roman nose and long ears.

Mubend and Read Sokoto - Quality skins in fine moroccan leather.

ORIGIN AND NATURE OF GOATS

Goats originate from warm, dry desert areas and mountainous terrain. Goats can stand more heat than sheep. They have a strong dislike for being in water and are reluctant to feed in the rain, so they should have shelter for loafing and feeding . Goats are very inquisitive, restless animals and can at times be mischievous. Goats are very selective eaters and will preferably eat the more nutritious leaves of plants rather than stem and leaf as do the cows. The goat more thoroughly chews and digests its feed in comparison to a cow. Goats also retain about a third more body water than cows. For these reasons, goats can thrive in areas where feed and water conditions would not maintain cows.[4]

STRESS

Goats are particularly affected by stress such as hauling, surgical operations, very hot weather, too much rain, shows and sales, etc. Stress will often trigger an attack of a disease or parasitism.

WATER

One must have a constant supply of clean, fresh water. Goats are very fastidious. Dirty water, strange tasting water, or water that is too warm or too cold cause a lower water consumption which can contribute to certain diseases.

HERD HEALTH: Vaccinations, Worming and Supplements

Preventive medicine is the key. Particular attention should be paid to nutrition, housing, sanitation and vaccination. Since goats are the most aggressive of all farm animals and have the most strict social order, they need relatively more feeding space than other species of animals. They should have 1½ to 2 ft. per head for feeder space. "Social Order" is important. The shy animal can actually starve to death by being pushed away from its feed by other goats that are more aggressive.

RECOMMENDED SCHEDULE FOR WORMING, VACCINES, ETC. FOR GOATS

The annual series of treatments for a good preventive medicine program for goat-worming, (antihelminthics), vaccinations and supplements should be considered. The following schedule is recommended.[5]

OCCASION	ACTIVITY
BREEDING DOES	
A. 4 weeks before BREEDING	Deworm, Vaccinate: Clostridium C & D Vitamin A & D
B. 2-4 weeks before KIDDING	Deworm, Vaccinate: Clostridium C & D Tetanus Toxoid, Vitamin E/Selenium
C. 2 weeks after kidding	Deworm
BREEDING BUCKS	
A. 4 weeks before breeding	Deworm, Vaccinate: Clostridium C & D, Tetanus Toxoid, Vitamin A & D Vitamin E/Selenium

KIDS

A. 4 weeks of age	Deworm
B. 8 weeks of age	Deworm, Vitamin E/Selenium
	Start Coccidiostat in areas where problem is common
C. 12 weeks of age	Deworm, Vaccinate: 2nd Tetanus Toxoid 2nd Clostridium C & D, Vitamin A & D

JUVENILES

Above 4 Months but Less Than 1 year	Deworm every 2 to 3 months

YEARLINGS

A. 1 year of age	Deworm every 2 to 3 months, Vaccinate: Clostridium C & D Tetanua Toxoid, Vitamin A & D Vitamin E/Selenium

OTHER ADULT CLASSES

B. Bucks, Does and Wethers	Deworm every 2 to 3 months, unless more frequent deworming is indicated in the schedule Vaccinate annually as for yearlings above

Note: Consider giving rabies vaccinations to goats where it is a real and constant danger to people. Also, not infrequently, Clostridium C & D vaccinations will require boosters every 6 months to maintain adequate immunity.

Clostridium perfringens types C and D (overeating disease) and tetanus toxoid combination vaccine is available and may be used in place of just Clostridium, C, D, using the same schedule. The 5- or 7-way clostridial vaccines may be necessary in some problem areas, but the cost is 5 to 6 times greater and vaccine reactions may be a problem when this cattle vaccine is used in goats.

Tetanus protection is essential at the time of disbudding and, or castration. Does vaccinated by this program pass immunity through their colostrum to the kids. Kids fed cow's colostrum should receive Clostridium perfringens type C and D antitoxin and tetanus at disbudding. Thereafter, kids may be put on the same vaccination program as recommmended above.

TETANIC SPASM

Soremouth vaccine is used only on premises with recurrent infections. Vaccinated kids become contagious, so animals should not be sent to other herds until the scabs are gone. See "Soremouth" under Chapter XII.

The worming schedule recommended is for animals maintained on dry lots. Those on irrigated pasture will require more frequent worming.

A coccidiostat for kids should be continued from 1 week of age until 2 to 4 weeks after weaning; the actual schedule will be determined by manufacture's labeled recommendations.

1. General information in this chapter is derived from *"Health Care of the Goat and Sheep"*, by R.A. Vanderhoof, VMD, 1987.

2. Extension Goat Handbook, A-1, Page 5.

3. Extension Goat Handbook - Fact Sheet A-1, Page 2.

4. Tulare County Goat Newsletter, University of California, Cooperative Ex—tension, Tom Shultz, Dairy Farm Advisor.

5. Dr. Nancy East, University of California, Davis.

Section 2

Normal Goat Physiological Data and Tables

PARTS OF A GOAT

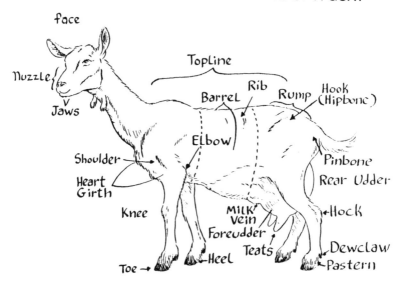

II. NORMAL GOAT PHYSIOLOGICAL DATA AND TABLES[1]

Rectal temperature: 104 degrees + or - 1 f. 40 degrees C.
Heartbeat (pulse) rate: 70 to 80 per minute, faster for kids.
Respiration rate: 12 to 15 per minute, faster for kids
Rumen movements in and out: 1 to 1.5 per minute
Onset of heat when (estrus) first starts: 7 to 12 months of age, depending on nutritional regime.
Length of the heat period: 12 to 48 hours - average about 1 day,
Heat cycle (estrous cycle) length of time between heat periods: 17 to 23 days - average 21 days
Length of pregnancy (gestation): 148 to 156 days - average 150 days
　　The total blood volume in the goat is 60 to 70 ml of blood per kilogram of body weight. If 1/3 of the blood volume is lost in a short time, shock ensues and death may result.

A. TEMPERATURE
Temperature Conversions=Rectal

	F	C
Subnormal	100.4	38.0
	101.3	38.5
	102.2	39.0
Normal*	103.1	39.5
	104.0	40.0
	104.9	40.5
Slight Fever	105.8	41.0
	106.7	41.5
High Fever	107.6	42.0
	or higher	

Conversion of Celsius to Fahrenheit: F - (x9/5)+32
Conversion of Fahrenheit to Celsius: C= (F-32)x5/9
*The body temperature is related to stress, exercise, and the enviromental temperature. If the goat is excited, has been severely exercised, or if it is a very hot, humid day, let the animal calm down and retake the temperature.

B. GESTATION TABLE[2]
(length of pregnancy average = 150 days)

Breeding Date		Kidding Date		Breeding Date		Kidding Date	
January	1	May	30	July	5	December	1
	6	June	4		10		6
	11		9		15		11
	16		14		20		16
	21		19		25		21
	26		24		30		26
	31		29	August	4		31
February	5	July	4		9	January	5
	10		9		14		10
	15		14		19		15
	20		19		24		20
	25		24		29		25
March	2		29	September	3		30
	7	August	3		8	February	4
	12		8		13		9
	17		13		18		14
	22		18		23		19
	27		23		28		24
April	1		28	October	3	March	1
	6	September	2		8		6
	11		7		13		11
	16		12		18		16
	21		17		23		21
	26		22		28		26
May	1		27	November	2		31
	6	October	2		7	April	5
	11		7		12		10
	16		12		17		15
	21		17		22		20
	26		22		27		25
	31		27	December	2		30
June	5	November	1		7	May	5
	10		6		12		10
	15		11		17		15
	20		16		22		20
	25		21		27		25
	30		28		31		30

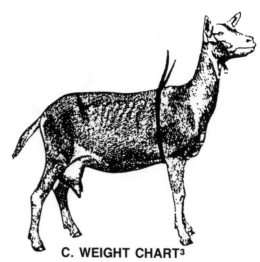

C. WEIGHT CHART[3]

To estimate the weight of a goat, measure the goat around the heart girth (pull the tape lightly) and consult the following chart:

Inches	Centimeters	Pounds	Kg.
10 3/4	27.3	5 1/2	2.27
11 1/4	28.8	5 1/2	2.49
11 3/4	29.9	6	2.73
12 1/4	31.1	6 1/2	2.95
12 3/4	32.4	7	3.17
13 1/4	33.7	8	3.63
13 3/4	34.9	9	4.08
14 1/4	36.2	10	4.54
14 3/4	37.5	11	4.99
15 1/4	38.7	12	5.44
15 3/4	40.0	13	5.90
16 1/4	41.3	15	6.40
16 3/4	42.7	17	7.71
17 1/4	43.8	19	8.62
17 3/4	45.1	21	9.52
18 1/4	46.4	23	10.43
18 3/4	47.6	25	11.34
19 1/4	48.9	27	12.24
19 3/4	50.2	29	13.15
20 1/4	51.4	31	14.06
20 3/4	52.7	33	14.97
21 1/4	53.9	35	15.87
21 3/4	55.3	37	16.78
22 1/4	56.5	39	17.69
22 3/4	57.8	42	19.05

Inches	Centimeters	Pounds	Kg.
23 1/4	59.1	45	20.41
23 3/4	60.3	48	21.77
24 1/4	61.6	51	23.13
24 3/4	62.9	54	24.49
25 1/4	64.1	57	25.85
25 3/4	65.4	60	27.21
26 1/4	66.7	63	28.57
26 3/4	66.7	66	29.93
27 1/4	69.2	69	31.29
27 3/4	70.5	72	32.65
28 1/4	71.7	75	34.01
28 3/4	73.0	78	35.37
29 1/4	74.3	81	36.73
29 3/4	75.6	84	38.10
30 1/4	76.8	87	39.46
30 3/4	78.0	90	40.82
31 1/4	79.4	93	42.18
31 3/4	80.7	97	44.00
32 1/4	81.9	101	45.80
32 3/4	83.2	105	47.62
33 1/4	84.5	110	49.89
33 3/4	85.7	115	52.15
34 1/4	87.0	120	54.42
34 3/4	88.3	125	56.69
35 1/4	89.5	130	58.96
35 3/4	90.6	135	61.22
36 1/4	92.1	140	63.49
36 3/4	93.4	145	65.76
37 1/4	94.6	150	68.08
37 3/4	95.9	155	70.29
38 1/4	97.2	160	74.83
38 3/4	98.4	165	77.10
39 1/4	99.7	170	79.37
39 3/4	101.0	175	81.63
40 1/4	102.2	180	83.90
40 3/4	103.5	185	86.17
41 1/4	104.8	190	87.30
41 3/4	106.1	195	88.44

1. Charts and tables derived from *"Health Care of the Goat and Sheep"*, R.A. Vanderhoof, VMD, 1987.
2. Penn State University, Dairy Goat Correspondence, Course No. 105.
3. Adapted from Ralston Company

Section 3

Owners Examination for Sickness

III. OWNER'S EXAMINATION FOR SICKNESS[1]

One should be able to recognize a sick goat in the early stages of a disease process.

Most diseases take from 3 to 5 days to cause death or spread to others.

Early diagnosis is essential. It is helpful to use a notebook or clipboard to record all salient observations to aid in a proper diagnosis. All goats should be observed at least daily.

Check for any animals that are lagging behind the herd, have a poor appetite, diarrhea, limping, breathing hard or fast, grunting, grinding of teeth, or other unusual behavior.

Examination Checklist (Make List)

1. Look at animal from a distance. Note the general condition and age of the goat. Can it stand and walk normally? Can it see (bumping into objects)? Does it exhibit signs of pain? Is it bloated? Are there swollen areas? Count respirations per minute (in and out).

2. Approach the animal. It should be held by an assistant by the neck or body. Do not run or fight the goat which might get excitable as will cause false temperature and respiration. The goat can be laid down on its side if it struggles.

3. Temperature. Shake down the thermometer. Insert into goat's rectum and leave for at least 1 minute.

4. Place your fingertips in front of left hip to feel rumen activity. It should move in and out about 1 to 1½ times per minute. If rumen sounds slushy, water-filled or distended with gas - note, it could be bloat, or an overloaded rumen from overeating grain.

5. Place fingertips on both sides of lower rib cage to feel for heartbeat and heart rate. The pulse can also be detected inside the upper rear leg. Count for 1 minute.

6. Roll back eyelids and lips of mouth to observe color of mucous membrane. Pink is normal; white could indicate anemia (lack of adequate number of red blood cells). Check color inside the vulva. "Angry" red: high fever, a serious malady, possibly.

7. Straddle the animal and feel over the goat's body for swelling or signs of pain.

8. Check for blindness. Move a hand toward the eye to detect blinking.

9. Note any unusual sounds, wheezing, coughing - respiratory problems. Grinding teeth or grunting - general body pain in the chest or abdomen.

10. Check all body openings to determine diarrhea, excessive salivation, or runny nose and whether clear or cloudy. Examine for crusty or runny eyes.

11. When examining a lactating (nursing) doe, always check the udder. Look for clots, or bloody or any off color abnormal milk. Feel for hard lumps, heat or signs of painful udder.

12. Detect any abnormal sounds of the abdomen and chest areas. A stethoscope should be used or place your ear against the goat's chest or abdomen.

13. Use the skin pinch test to determine roughly the degree of dehydration if the animal is very sick.

Skin ridge formed 5% - moderate

Skin ridge persists for length of time 10% - serious - will probably not live long.

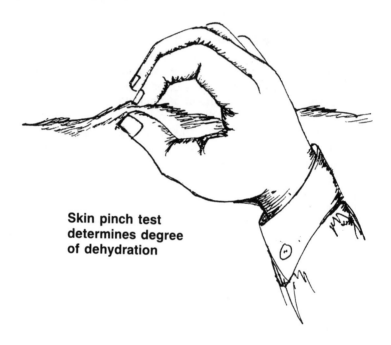

**Skin pinch test
determines degree
of dehydration**

14. Condition of skin and hair coat is a good indicator of general health. Examine hair condition for roughness, lack of luster, hair ends split, and turned up - "scroungy looking." This often is caused by parasitism. Sickness can be the cause also as well as mineral/vitamin deficiency.

15. Have animals been transported recently? How far and from where?

16. Condition of pasture. Were insecticides or herbicides used? If so, what and when?

17. What are feeding, grazing/browsing habits? Is there need for roughage in the diet?

18. Goats can have ear mites causing shaking of head.

19. Examine feet. Hooves should not be overgrown. Hooves will have a characteristic odor if have infection. This is known as foot rot.

20. Examine all joints by palpation (by feeling with your fingers).

21. Mammary glands (the udder or "bag")—examine for lumps and whether one side is warmer than other. Examine teats for patency (being open) in lactating (milking) animals, especially right after they give birth.

GOOD HEALTH PROGRAM

1. Good nutrition is essential. Hay and pasture and browse for forage, protein and energy supplements and plenty of fresh water.

2. Exercise.

3. Adequate internal and external parasite control.

4. An adequate vaccination program.

5. Daily observation.

6. Plentiful fresh water supply

7. A supply of clean loose salt (coarse granulated) and minerals. Do not use salt blocks for goats; they will probably not get enough.

A plentiful supply of fresh water all all times is very important

1. Material derived from *"Health Care of the Goat and Sheep"*, R.A. Vanderhoof, VMD, 1987.

Section 4

Emergencies and Preventive Management

IV. EMERGENCIES AND PREVENTIVE MANAGEMENT[1]

No matter how careful you are as a goat owner/breeder and how well managed your premises are, there will be veterinary emergency situations. All of the items below should probably require veterinary assistance.

EMERGENCIES

a) Rectal temperature that is very high - 106 degrees F (41.1C) or very low and depressed temperature - 100 degrees F (37.7 C) or less could mean impending death. If temperature is taken on a hot day with an animal that is struggling, its temperature might conceivably be 106 degrees F (41.1 C). So you must allow for this. Goats do not generally deal calmly with pain or stress.

b) Difficulty in breathing - open mouth, panting or difficult inhaling.

c) Wounds that penetrate a joint or tendon sheath. Immediate attention is necessary.

d) Eye infections or wounds that can cause permanent damage and blindness.

e) Shock. Typical signs are:
1] cold extremities, warm or cool body
2]. pale mucous membranes, pale gums
3] rapid, weak heart beat
4] loss of skin elasticity
5] subnormal body temperature, shivering
6] recumbent animal, too weak to get up
7] causes of shock frequently apparent; for example, watery diarrhea, severe hemorrhage, adverse reaction to a drug.

f) Birth of a very weak or premature kid that has become seriously chilled. Should provide a source of warmth. Place in warm water bath if its body temperature is below 96 degrees F, (35.5 degrees C,) until normal temperature is restored, then dry thoroughly and quickly. For energy - give colostrum or milk.

g) Tremors, convulsions, coma. Use vitamin B_1 (Thiamine) - 1 to 2 cc IM.

h) Uterine prolapse. Cleanse with disinfectant soap and gently replace. Place 500 mg. of ampicillin or tetracycline in uterus.

i) Wounds especially those penetrate the chest or abdominal cavities. Cover completely and tightly. Veterinary assistance is advised.

j) Difficult urination - straining, dribbling, blood tinged urine or complete absence of urine. Usually caused by urinary or bladder stones. Feeding ammonium chloride will help prevent this.

k) Bloat - make a small incision through skin on the left side - above flank on the left side between the last rib and the hip. Insert the trocar through incision, on into paunch (rumen) by directing instrument toward the opposite (right) front foot. Remove trocar, leaving the metal sheath in place (in rumen) to allow the escape of accumulated gas. Fortunately, bloating occurs much less frequently in goats than in cattle. A small tube may also be passed down the throat into the rumen to release the gas.

TROCAR

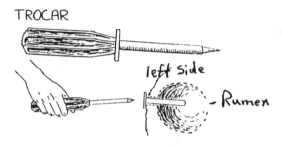

left side

- Rumen

l) Nervous symptoms, e.g., circling, sudden blindness, tilted head, and "star gazing" -probably nervous system affected. Inject Thiamin hydrochloride, which is Vitamin B_1, ½ to 1 cc IM.

m) Abdominal distress - grinding teeth, distended abdomen and kicking abdomen - offer water, no food.

n) Abnormal feces - absence of feces, changes in color and consistency, mucous or blood in feces, diarrhea which rapidly dehydrates the animal, especially the young. See previous pages on kid diarrhea.

o) Uncontrolled bleeding - employ a pressure bandage. Wrap the bleeding wound with bandage or any available cloth sufficiently tight to stop the hemorrhage.

p) Pinkeye - can be contagious. Remove any foreign body. Use an eye antibiotic, e.g., tetracycline or chloromycetin. With pinkeye it is best to keep the animal out of the direct sunlight, wind and dust.

q) Poisoning (See section on poisons below).

PHYSICAL INJURY/WOUNDS/BURNS/FRACTURES

Goats are often injured in fights with dogs, predators, and other goats. Usually, with a little help, the animal will heal itself. First, bleeding should be stopped. This can normally be done by applying mild pressure. Second, clean the wound with mild soap and water or hydrogen peroxide. Remove all dirt, hair, and trash. Be gentle so as not to cause renewed bleeding. Next, apply an antibiotic ointment, cream or powder to the area. Finally, apply a bandage if the damaged area is large, and give antibiotic injections daily for a week, e.g., Penicillin or ampicillin, 5 cc - 1M - twice daily for 4 to 10 days, depending on severity of infection. Most wounds do not require bandaging. Protect from fly infestation (screw worms). Also clean and protect burned area with an ointment. Use a saline or salt solution, 1 teaspoon per pint of water, for cleaning and do not damage the burned area. If no antibiotic ointment is available, butter or cream will help. Any cream medication you would use on yourself could be used on burns or wounds.

If the wounds or burns are severe and large areas of skin are destroyed, the goat probably should be slaughtered. Fractures and dislocations sometimes are seen when goats fight or get entangled in fences, feeders, or other equipment. Usually, it is best to slaughter as soon as possible after the break occurs.

PREVENTIVE MANAGEMENT

a) Keep all concentrates (grain, pellets, etc.) under lock! Goats are smart enough to open some latches. An overloaded stomach can cause death.

b) Use good, adequate fencing to prevent dog or wild animal attacks. Sentinel dogs, donkeys, or llamas may also be used to keep away wild animals. Avoid barbed wire to prevent lacerations.

c) Keep wire, pieces of metal or glass, etc., out of your goat pens and watch out for projecting nails or bolts.

d) Provide adequate space for each animal, especially when there are aggressive and dominant animals in your herd. This is important when there is an age or size difference in the herd.

e) It can be dangerous to pen goats with larger species of livestock, e.g., cattle or horse, even though some goats seem to keep horses company and vice versa.

f) Keep animal off roads. Honk your horn if you come upon any animal or bird in the roadway.

g) Avoid sudden changes in feed to prevent diarrhea.

h) Always provide a clean fresh source of water, especially during freezing weather.

i) It pays to regularly inspect your goat housing area and management practices for harmful details. Do not assume that everything is all right!

j) Keep poisonous plants and chemicals out of premises.

k) Provide shelter from rain and cold weather. Goats do not like a wet, cold environment.

1. Material derived from *"Health Care of the Goat and Sheep"*, R.A. Vanderhoof, VMD, 1987.

Section 5

Recommended Veterinary Medical Supplies and Equipment

V. RECOMMENDED VETERINARY MEDICAL SUPPLIES AND EQUIPMENT

1. Rectal thermometer (keep in cool or cold place).
2. Roll of absorbent cotten, adhesive tape and gauze pads, gauze rolls, Ace bandage and/or Vetrap.
3. Hypodermic syringes and needles.
4. Baking soda, magnesium sulfate (epsom salts), and mineral oil.
5. Antibiotics e.g., Oxytetracycline, Sulfamethazine, Naxel (Upjohn) Nuflor (Schering - Plough), Ampicillin, Chloromycetin or tetracycline eye ointment.
6. Antibacterial solutions, e.g., Betadine Solution and Betadine Scrub or Nolvasan.
7. Scalpel (a surgical knife).
8. Epinephrine (Adrenalin).
9. Dexamethasone (Azium - a cortico - steroid).
10. Hoof shears and hoof nippurs.
11. Hoof knife.
12. Sulfa compounds for use in drinking water.
13. Trocar.
14. Thiamin Hydrochloride (Vitamin B1) for neurological symptoms.
15. Cyanocobalamin (Vitamin B12) - to improve appetite; to combat anemia.
16. Bo-SE-(Selenium-Vitamin E combination).
17. The Merck Veterinary Manual Published by: Merck and Co., Inc., Rahway, NJ, USA.

Section

Poisons

VI. POISONS[1]

PLANTS

Goats are browsers and tolerate more bitter-tasting plants than will other species. The natural behavior of the wild goat, eating only those plants chosen by the experienced doe leader, results in few plant poisonings. Kids raised away from the herd will not learn this protective behavior. The backyard goat, especially one confined in a small wooded area or allowed into the flower garden, is at risk. Goats lacking salt or natural browse may be more apt to eat deadly plants. Also to be avoided is the practice of discarding garden or hedge clippings within reach of the inquisitive goat. The best way to protect a goat from a tree or vice versa is to wrap chicken wire two or three times around the trunk to a height of 6 feet. The wire will need to be adjusted every 6 years or so as the tree grows.

GENERAL RULE: Animals generally will not eat poisonous plants if there is plenty of grazing and forage available to them.

The following is a partial list of plants known or suspected to be poisonous to goats:

Belladonna - Atropa (Deadly Nightshade) - has killed goats, incoordination, convulsions, loss of function of stomach.

Buttercup - Ranunculus - reported in goats, oral tissues fiery red. Salivation, diarrhea, abdominal pain.

Castor beans and plant.

Cocklebur - Xanthium - seed leaves contain hydroquinone; vomit, depression, heavy breathing, unsteady gait, head thrown back and rigid.

Cyanide Poisoning - Johnson grass/Sudan grass/sorghum - new growth after damage to the plant, e.g., freezing and drought or herbicide application (less than 1 foot high) produces HCN, (hydrocyanic acid), a very quick acting poison also known as prussic acid. Symptoms: respiratory distress, blue mucous membranes, muscle tremors, convulsions, death. The animal's tissues are usually bright red.

Locoweed - Astragalus - loco reported in goats results in loss of condition, staggering, ataxia, constipation.

Milkweed.

Oak - Quercus - acorns or buds contain tannins. Symptoms: abdominal distress, gaunt, weak, constipation or diarrhea. Large numbers of acorns will poison goats quite readily.

Oleander - all parts of the plant are toxic and there is no treatment.

Poison Hemlock - Conium - reported in goats; nervousness, trembling, staggering, weak pulse, cold extremities, coma, death.

Poison oak - goats and cattle eat and relish poison oak without any ill effects. It seems that the milk from such a doe is perfectly okay to use.

Potato parings - Poisonous principle: solanin. Nervous or digestive disorder, diarrhea, paralysis, dyspnea, weak pulse, death.

Rhododendron, Mountain laurel - Kalmia. Symptoms: frothing, vomiting, depression, staggering, colic, grinding teeth.

Rhubarb - Rheum - oxalates in blade toxic to all classes of livestock; danger if leaves thrown to animals. Treat with fluids and calcium.

Water Hemlock - Cicuta - "all livestock" - roots and shoots, especially in spring when loose in ground; frothing at the mouth, violent convulsions, death.

Plants Which Cause Photosensitivity - (reaction to sunlight). The important plants involved in this group are buckwheat, alsike clover, rape, St. John's wort, and to a lesser extent, ladino and white clover. With the exception of St. John's wort, all of the plants are quite palatable and nutritious. White-skinned animals eating enough of these plants (those that produce lush growth in ideal weather are the worst) in bright sunny weather develop anything from sunburn to severe sloughing of the white-skinned areas.

There are three basic requirements for development of photosensitivity when goats eat these plants: the animals must have white skin, the animals must eat a minimum quantity of the plants, and they must be exposed to bright sunlight for at least one-half day all at the same time.

CHEMICAL AND MINERAL

Arsenic - insecticides and weed-killers are the major sources. Signs are usually severe gastroenteritis (inflammation of stomach and intestines) and abdominal pain, fetid diarrhea and death.

Chlorinated Hydrocarbons - Benzene hexachloride group; includes lindane, dieldrin, chlordane. These chemicals are found in the meat and excreted in the milk for a long time after exposure. Young goats are quite susceptible; a .15% dip twice at 4 day intervals has been reported to kill; more than .3% is toxic to adult goats. Young, emaciated (thin), or lactating (milking) animals are more susceptible. Signs usually appear within 24 hours and include neuromuscular (nerve and muscle) disorders; apprehension, hypersensitivity, blepharospasm (twitching of the eyelids), muscle faciculations (trembling movement) and spasms, increased salivation and chewing movements, convulsions and death due to respiratory failure (failure of lung function). Sometimes severe depression is noted instead. Wash with cold water to remove further toxin from the skin and then lower the body temperature (if convulsing).

Haloxon - in sheep and cattle posterior paralysis may appear suddenly or several weeks after worming.

Lead - sources include paint cans, licking painted boards, car batteries, used car oil and certain automotive lubricants, and boiled linseed oil. Poisoning is rare in goats, which are much more resistant to lead than are cattle. Symptoms: Loss of appetite, dullness, diarrhea or constipation.

Organophosphates used for external and internal parasite control in various animal species. Signs of toxicity are salivation and excessive tears, open-mouth breathing, protrusion of tongue, colic, abdominal pain, pupillary (closing down of the eyes) constriction, stiffness, staggering gait, bloat, and death due to respiratory failure. Toxic compounds include trithion, diazon, coumaphos (CO-RAL), fenthion, malathion, and Ronnel (fenchlorphos). 100 mg/kg is the maximum safe oral dose of fenchlorphos in goats.

Phenothiazine - may cause abortion. Red colored milk and urine may result.

Ethylene glycol (Prestone) - antifreeze draining from automobile radiator. Animals will drink because it is sweet. Causes irreparable damage to the kidneys and then death.

Salt - poisoning may occur if animals eat too much because they were previously deprived of salt or if they drink saline water. Signs are thirst, salivation, and GI (stomach and intestinal) disturbance.

OTHERS

Allergies - Caused by insect or spider stings, injections, or applications of certain medications to the skin.

Snake Bites: Treatment of snake bite depends largely on the class of venomous snake. Keeping in mind that every snake is not poisonous, it follows that identification of the snake is very important. In species which are very poisonous, e.g., the pit vipers, snake bite often results in the death of the animal unless treated correctly and promptly. Thus, if one witnesses the event of the bite and identifies the snake as poisonous, a qualified veterinarian should be consulted, if available, before the animal shows signs of illness. The bite of non-poisonous species needs to be treated as any other dirty wound, with diligent cleaning and wound care, perhaps including antibiotics-such as penicillin with dihydrostreptomycin. In all cases of snake bite, make sure the animal is protected against tetanus, ideally by the use of routine annual revaccination with tetanus toxoid. When professional veterinary services are not available, the bite of poisonous snakes can be treated with the administration of antibiotics. If the animal is in shock, give him a one time dose of 5 - 50 cc of dexamethazone IV or IM, depending on the size of the animal, and keep him calm and warm. Then give 1/2 -1 cc every four to six hours until the swelling starts to subside. Slowely reduce the frequency over a two week period by lengthening the interval betweem injections until you are giving 1/2 cc every other day. Stop after three such injections. Administer antibiotics appropriately.

Section 7

Digestive System

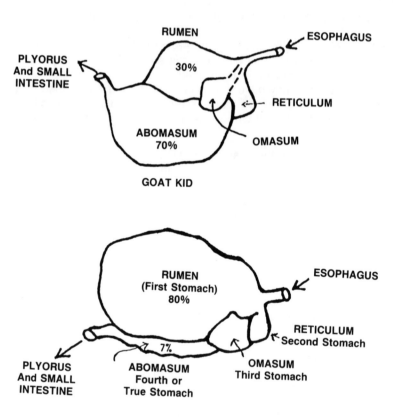

GOAT KID

ADULT GOAT

The four stomach compartments of young and adult goats, showing relative changes in dimensions from pre-ruminant to ruminant status. Drawing courtesy of D. L. Ace, Pennsylvania State University.

VII. DIGESTIVE SYSTEM[1]

A Brief Anatomy and Physiology of the Gastrointestinal (G.I.) Tract of the Ruminant:

The small ruminants, goats and sheep, are polygastric like the cow in that they have four stomachs; the rumen or paunch, reticulum, omasum, and abomasum. The foundation for good goat feeding is an understanding of rumen function.

The first stomach, or rumen, where microorganism digestion takes place, is virtually a large fermentation vat with a capacity of 3 to 5 gallons, where the ground or chewed up hay and grain with water is attacked by billions of beneficial bacteria and protozoa. These "microscopic bugs" break down the tough plant fibers so they can be digested, and also manufacture all the vitamins except vitamin A and possibly vitamin E. They also make a number of the amino acids - the precursors, (beginners) of the formation, of protein - for the animal.

Gas is formed in the rumen constantly by these microorganisms, so the animal must belch about every 20 minutes. If not, it will bloat, (fill up with gas), and die by suffocation in about ½ to 1 hour. The animal obtains vitamin A from green plants or green hay and it is stored in the liver for a 3 - to 6 - month period.

Herbivores (plant-eating animals) manufacture copious amounts of saliva, enabling them to swallow and digest dry grasses and foliage. (A cow can produce 2 to 3 gallons of saliva per day). Goats and sheep chew their cud while resting - regurgitating a small amount of ingesta from the first stomach, chewing it 30 to 40 times, then swallowing. The cud travels into the second stomach, the reticulum, where it is mixed with juices and macerated, and ground up (this is the "honey comb" stomach). Food then travels into and through the third stomach, the omasum "manypiles" where it is further macerated and ground up still finer. Then into the fourth stomach, the abomasum - or the true stomach - which is shaped much like ours. This is where much of the enzyme digestion takes place before passing on into the small and large intestines for additional digestion. Nutrients are picked up by the bloodstream along much of the GI tract, mostly the intestines.

When a ruminant fails to chew its cud, it is usually a sign that peristalsis (movement) of the GI (stomach-intestinal) tract has slowed or ceased. All food, but not water, should be withheld until this condition has been rectified. Many animals can be simply cured this way. After animal again becomes hungry, then hay and concentrates should be added back gradually in small increments over the next 2 or 3 days, resuming the normal ration.

In normal peristalsis, put your ear to left side of abdomen of animal over the rumen, and you should hear bubbling, gurgling sounds inside. If impacted, there is very little or no sound.

Rumen stimulation:
1. Torumen - a dried yeast powder
2. Acidophilus bacteria in an oral paste.
3. The cud material can be transferred to another animal by reaching into the mouth of a healthy ruminating animal and retrieving the mass. Dilute with water and drench a sick animal with this.

The digestive system of goats and all other ruminants is designed physiologically to handle forages with a minimum of grain, fruits, etc. Too many dairy goat owners feed their animals diets which would be more appropriate for pigs - too much grain and not enough forage. A kid or lamb won't start chewing its cud until its rumen develops - at birth. Goats of any age will eat more feed and waste less if they are fed small quantities at frequent intervals.

DIGESTION

Goats are fastidious eaters and can distinguish bitter, salt, sweet, and sour. They have a higher threshold for bitter than cows, but probably lower than camels. They have a pronounced sweet taste. They reject salt at concentration of 5 gm/100 ml. Goats do more browsing than other ruminants; they may spend 46% of the day eating and may cover 6 miles per day while foraging. They tend to strip a pasture. Goats eat more species of plants than do sheep. Goats eat to keep warm and stop eating to prevent hypertoxemia (overeating), when out on the pasture or range. They will overeat however, if they gain access to grain - often fatally!

FEEDING

The Goat is related to the deer. Since it is a browser as well as a grazer, it would rather reach up than down for food. The goat also craves variety. Coupled with this is the goat's natural curiosity and nothing is safe from at least a trial taste.

Anything hanging, like clothes on the line, is just too much for a goat's natural instinct. Rose bushes and pine trees are high in vitamin C and goats love them. Leaves, branches, and bark of young trees are a natural part of the goat's diet.

Pulling Clothes Off Line

Their digestive tract is especially adapted to consuming leaves and brush and will do better if allowed access while feeding hay and grain.

Allow goats to graze or browse in the pasture for 8 hours per day. If you have no fenced pasture, tether in grassy places. Use of "zero" pasture management is very workable and recommended. See under Chapter X.

Feed concentrates (grain), for readily available source of energy and protein. They especially need this if they are young and growing, or if they are milking does, or for bucks that are breeding, or if you want to fatten wethers for butchering.

Provide a salt supply. Keep it clean, as goats are fastidious and won't like dirty salt. Salt blocks for licking will do, but since goats have a smooth tongue, they will get more salt if it is in granualr form. A combination of salt and mineral preparation is recommended.

1. Material derived from *"Health Care of the Goat and Sheep"*, R.A. Vanderhoof, VMD, 1987.

Section

Nutrition

The Salt Lick

VIII. NUTRITION

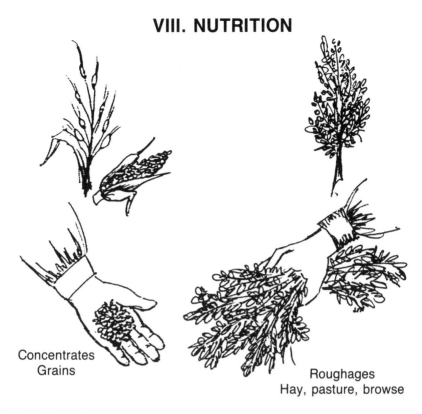

Concentrates
Grains

Roughages
Hay, pasture, browse

Note: The differentiation between concentrates (cereal grains for the most part) and roughage (hay, pasture, and browse) must be understood. Roughages consist of the entire plant and are higher in fiber than concentrates.

ESSENTIALS FOR A BALANCED AND PALATABLE RATION

1. **Storage and age** of forage: goats steadfastly refuse to eat musty or dusty hay. Such hay usually contains a tremendous amount of mold. Most molds in hay, if not downright toxic, are an irritant to the digestive tract or the respiratory tract when ingested.

2. **Quality of protein**: Good hay - alfalfa or other kinds of legume hay. Three or four different kinds of grain. A wide variety is advisable.

3. **Palatability**: Feeds must be well liked. They should be from a variety of sources - 3 to 7 different plant sources. Forage intake can often be greatly improved in goats being fed the best of hays if some supplementary green forage is fed at least once daily. Hand harvested green legumes, surplus vegetables from the garden, surplus fruits like apples or pears, comfrey, turnips, pumpkins, etc. are welcome additions to the daily diet as they apparently improve digestion and appetite for the stable diet.

4. **Minerals**: Calcium and phosphorus are the two essentials - "Ca" and "P". Ca from legume hays, e.g., alfalfa. P from wheat bran and oil meals. All livestock need salt, preferable loose, instead of blocks.

5. **Bulkiness or fiber**: Roughage is essential for all ruminants. Grain mixture should not be out of proportion to the roughage. Half or more of the diet should be roughage. About 30% concentrates (grain) is desirable. A goat may eat as much as 11% of her body weight as dry matter per day. Five to eight pounds dry matter per 100 lbs. body weight per day is a common capacity. Increased fiber is necessary in cold weather to maintain body temperature. Too little fiber predisposes to enterotoxemia. Clostridium perfringens organisms are always present in the digestive tract, but rapid overgrowth and toxin (poison) production occurs with high grain feeding or sudden changes in diet. Goats that suddenly engorge on grain are also prone to toxic ingestion, with severe metabolic acidosis (acidic condition of the system), dehydration, and splashy sounds (excess fluid present) in the rumen. Vigorous fluid and electrolyte (chemicals of the body) replacement will be needed to save these animals. Dry matter must be adequate. Animals can graze on succulent new growth grass and actually lose weight because of the high water content.

6. **Variety**: Goats prefer many more species of plants than sheep or cows. They like elm, ash, hazel, willow and oak; also briars, ivy, pigweed, thistles, nettles, dock, mulberry leaves and bananas. Browsing habits result in a higher mineral uptake because the species eaten have deeper roots than do grasses. Variety improves palatability. There are many good forage crops in addition to alfalfa, such as peavine, lespedeza, improved bermuda, clover, timothy, etc.

7. **Right amount** for mature goat: A mature goat will require anywhere from three to ten pounds of hay per day depending on type, quality, waste, and other factors. Give grain according to amount of milk produced. For lactating (milking) animals, the protein content of the concentrate ration should be about 16% of the roughage. With less protein in hay, more must be added to the concentrate. For dry does, 12% protein is sufficient. The watchfulness by the herdsman is essential. **General Rule:** Whatever each animal can clean up in 15 minutes is about right.

RATION CHART

Ration for a milking doe fed good alfalfa hay.
12.6% digestible protein.

	LBS.	KG.
Corn	31	14
Oats	25	11.3
Wheat bran	11	4.95
Linseed oil meal	22	9.9
Cane molasses	10	4.5
Salt	1	.45

Ration for a milking doe fed good alfalfa hay.
12.6% digestible protein.

	LBS.	KG.
Barley	40	18
Oats	28	12.6
Wheat bran	10	4.5
Soybean oil meal	11	4.95
Cane molasses	10	4.5
Salt	1	.45

Ration for a milking doe fed non-legume hay.
21.2% digestible protein.

Corn	11	4.95
Oats	10	4.5
Wheat bran	10	4.5
Corn gluten feed	30	13.5
Soybean oil meal	11	4.95
Cane molasses	10	4.5
Salt	1	.45

Ration for a milking doe fed non-legume hay.
21.2% digestible protein

Barley	25	11.3
Wheat bran	10	4.5
Soybean oil meal	25	11.3
Linseed oil meal	15	6.75
Salt	1	.45

Ration for dry does and bucks.
9.6% digestible protein.

Corn	58	26.
Oats	25	11.3
Wheat bran	11	4.95
Soybean oil meal	5	2.25
Salt	1	.45

Ration for dry does and bucks.
10.1% digestible protein.

Barley or wheat	51½	23.5
Oats	35	15.75
Wheat bran	12½	5.6
Salt	1	.45

8. **Succulents**: Greater production and condition are gained from succulent feeds throughout the year. Root crops are good for goats, especially beets, turnips, cabbages, and carrots.

9. **Water:**

a. Water is the most important of all feeds for animals. It is impossible to have production efficiency and healthy animals where water quality is poor. Production in low-producing, health-problem dairy herds is often improved tremendously by providing a new or better source of water. Goats are more fussy about fouled water than any other animal. Slightly fouled water can reduce water intake tremendously and correspondingly cut milk production.

b. Water and shade are necessary. Place water troughs near and around goat sheds and pens. Hard water (high calcium, low phosphorus) may cause an increase in male infertility. Warming the water has been advised if feeding much concentrate. A dry diet with restricted water supply will fatten a goat. Adding salt to the water or the diet will increase the milk yield, but should only be done if the goats are too fat. Some breeders feed molasses water to the goats: ½ cup molasses in 12 quarts water is given routinely for its tonic effect. Molasses also helps to prevent ketosis (a disease in which the body burns up its own fat).

c. Every encouragement should be given to the lactating (milking) goat to drink large quantities of water. Milk is more than 85% water, so it is essential to supply adequate water to produce milk.

An adequate, clean water supply is important.

10. **Metabolic (functions of the body) cycle:** A sudden drop in milk yield and appetite occurs naturally in the fall. The production decreases to less than two quarts and the goat gains weight when the appetite again increases. A dry, high fiber diet is needed at this time. Does vary in production while cycling, and another decline occurs after the breeding season. Keep the goats thin during the first half of gestation, then increase feed as the fetus grows rapidly. Restricted water, a "dry" diet, and irregular milking will help to dry off a goat that doesn't do so by herself. Increase feed the last 8 weeks ("steaming up") to avoid pregnancy toxemia (poisons in the blood). Introduce moist feed like red wheat bran with enough water to make a mush or gruel, the last few days before kidding and return to a drier diet 3-4 days after kidding. A good milker will lose weight the first 4 months of lactation. Goats store fat preferentially in the abdominal cavity and by the time fat is grossly obvious, the internal deposits are substantial. This can lead to problems at kidding and to pregnancy toxemia.

11. **Cost:** A grain mix which will furnish the most digestible nutrients and the most protein per dollar to balance the roughage will be the most economical.

A. dry or pregnant doe will usually consume 1½ pounds grainfeed daily.

It is generally considered that 6 to 8 goats can be kept on the feed required for 1 cow.

Generally 500 pounds of hay and 450 pounds of grain are required for each mature goat per year.

If a doe does not receive sufficient Ca, (calcium) and P (phosphorus) in her ration while pregnant, these elements will be drawn from her bones and teeth in favor of the developing fetus.

Dry does - should be fed free choice hays - ½ high quality oat hay and ½ high quality alfalfa with 1 lb of grain per day. If very fat, reduce to ½ lb grain and cut down the alfalfa.

Milking does - (refer to the table above) feed ½ lb of grain per pound of milk. Increase the grain up to 3/4 lb as long as production increases, then back off the grain when milk production reaches a peak. By the fifth month of lactation, as little as 1 lb. of grain to 4 to 5 lbs. of milk may be fed. Expect does to lose weight during lactation. Pelleted feeds do not decrease butterfat content in goat's milk as they do in cattle.

OVERVIEW OF MINERALS

Seven major mineral elements are required by the mammalian body and constitute 60 to 80% of all inorganic matter in the body. These are calcium, magnesium, sodium, potassium, phosphorus, sulfur, and chlorine. These chemicals constitute what is known as electrolytes and are measured in milligrams per ml or lbs. One begins to see why electrolytes in the blood and cells are so important to maintain at the correct level.

Trace mineral elements are also found in the body and in extremely small amounts. They are very essential and are measured in ppm (parts per million). At least eight of these are iron, copper, iodine, manganese, cobalt, zinc, molybdenum, and selenium, and are especially important for good fertility.

Some "newer" mineral elements and their body requirements:
Chromium (Ci) = < 0.1 ppm
Nickel (Ni) = .03 to 3.0 ppm
Vanadium (V) = 0.1 ppm
Tin (Sn) = 1.5 to 2 ppm
Flourine (F) = 2.5 ppm
Silicon (Si) = 5 to 100 ppm

The microflora (plant life) and microfauna (animal life) of the goat rumen action initiate the breakdown of feedstuffs, especially the weedy portion.

With carbohydrates - grasses, hay, etc., cellulose (fiber) is further broken down into glucose by cellulose enzymes.

"Pica" - depraved appetite. Cause by deficiency of minerals and feed. Symptoms: chewing sticks, bones, stones, etc., loss of flesh, rough hair coat, or stiffness of body. Treatment: Make sure the ration contains the essential minerals, carbohydrates (corn, barley, wheat and proteins), (oil meals made from cotton seed, soybeans, etc.).

MINERAL PROPORTIONS/RATIONS

The calcium-phosphorus ratio is very important in nutrition. Dry does and bucks require a 1.5 to 1 ratio and lactating does require a 2 to 1 ratio.

Alfalfa hay often has a Ca:P ratio of 5:1. This results in articular (joint) Ca deposits -especially manifested in bucks that have Ca deposits in their joints. Does are not affected as much as they seem to eliminate Ca in their milk. Prevention: Mix oat hay and grains to balance out the ration.

Symptoms of Calcium deficiency:
1. "Milk fever" (paralysis).
2. Nerves are affected.
3. Bone structure is impaired.

Symptoms of Phosphorous deficiency:
1. Tendency to produce offspring only every other year.
2. Reduced milk production - a shorter milking period.
3. Bone disease manifestation and deformities.
4. Dental problems.

POSSIBLE MINERAL MIXES THAT MIGHT
BE PREPARED LOCALLY:

Mix No. 1 - Equal parts - ground limestone (or oyster shell)
- steamed bone meal
- trace mineralized salt (or iodized salt)

Mix No. 2 - Equal parts - ground limestone (or oyster shell)
- DiCalcium phosphate
- trace mineralized salt (or iodized salt)

Mix No. 3 - Equal parts - ground limestone (or oyster shell)
- Deflourinated Rock Phosphate
- trace mineralized salt (or iodized salt)

Mix No. 4 - Equal parts - steamed bone meal or DiCalcium phosphate
- trace mineralized salt

TRACE ELEMENTS

Iodine (I) deficiency - Availability is dependent on soil content, being highest in soils that hold moisture well, such as peats, clays, and humus-rich soils. Seaweed meal is high in iodine, or iodized salt may be fed. A milliliter of tincture of iodine painted on the skin of the nursing doe once a week will prevent goiters in the kids, but would not be necessary with an appropriate diet.

Goiter—enlarged neck from iodine deficiency

TRACE ELEMENTS DEFICIENCIES

Iodine. Absolutely essential for body functions in trace amounts for all animals and humans. Necessary for the manufacturing of thyroxine by the thyroid gland.

Symptoms of a deficiency:
1. Enlarged neck - thyroid gland
2. Kids born hairless or covered with small, fine hair.
3. Kids covered with thick, scaly skin.
4. Kids stillborn.

Treatment: See under text above on "Iodine Deficiency."

Iron (Fe) deficiency does not seem to be a problem with goats and sheep.

Salt: Be sure that salt is available for goats at all times. Use loose salt, as goats usually don't like the trace mineral blocks. The salt must be kept clean because goats, being so fastidious, will refuse it if dirty. Adult goats will eat about 10 grams of salt per day.

VITAMIN DEFICIENCIES

Hypovitaminosis A (lower than normal) = a deficiency of vitamin A.

Treatment: Green pasture or forage. Vitamin A injections. Vitamin deficiencies are sometimes a problem in marginal quality forage areas and multivitamin injections are especially valuable to sick and weak animals.

Selenium (se) and vitamin E (T): SeT = selenium tocopherol (tocopherol) is the chemical name for vitamin E. SeT deficiency syndrome. Until recently, little information as to the importance of Se and T has been known. Now they are known as essential elements. In soils, selenium (a metal and one of the elements) is often in short supply, so crops and grass are often deficient. This situation is widespread in most livestock producing areas. Selenium and vitamin E are absolutely essential for maintaining healthy livestock. The product to use is "Bo-Se", see appendix 1.

Prevention: Does - at time of breeding. Inject 1ml, one month prior to kidding. 2.5 ml per 100 lbs. body weight or 45.4 Kg. Bucks - 2.5 ml per 100 lbs. body weight or 45.4 Kg. once during breeding season, again 6 months later. Kids - Inject 1/4 ml per 40 lbs. body weight or 18 Kg. Repeat in 3 to 4 weeks. Discontinue 14 days before kid is slaughtered.

MISCELLANEOUS OBSERVATIONS ON NUTRITION

Overstocking and overgrazing pastures lead to serious health problems:
1. Animals not able to obtain enough TDN (Total Digestible Nutrients).
2. Often leads to severe intestinal parasite problems.

3. Especially harmful to the growth of good pasture grasses.
4. Causes extensive soil erosion.

Overstocking
Overgrazing

Anorexia - loss of appetite.
Treatment:
1. Inject vitamin B_{12} intramuscularly 2 or 3 times per week, using about ½ ml. IM
2. There is currently acidophilus (beneficial) bacterial available in the form of a paste and is given orally, BeneBac - bovine, or Probiocin - ruminant, or use soured milk.

Overeating - Keep grain (concentrates) under lock and key! Goats will break into a feed supply if they can and overeat. This causes an extreme emergency, often fatal.

Routine: Goats are fanatic creatures of habit, so adhere strictly to a daily routine.

Feed change Avoid abrupt changes in feeding grain and forage.

Cleanliness: Keep all feed and water facilities scrupulously clean.

Salt and Minerals: Salt and minerals should be added and the mixture fed loose. When blocks are fed, they may not get enough.

---

1. Material derived from *"Health Care of the Goat and Sheep"*, R.A. Vanderhoof, VMD, 1987.

Section 9

Housing and Fencing

IX. HOUSING AND FENCING[1]

It is dangerous to turn two mature bucks in together in the same pen suddenly. If raised together, it can be fairly safe if young, but if fully grown, they still can be dangerous to each other.

The majority of goats in this country are managed much the same as dairy cows. They require milking twice daily and the usual length of lactation is 305 days. This allows a 60-day dry period for the doe to replenish her body stores of nutrients before the next lactation. When a doe kids, or "freshens", it is common practice to remove the kids and raise them separately from their mothers.

Goats require protection from the elements. The shelter provided need not be elaborate but it must keep the animals clean and dry and away from drafts. Many older buildings can be adapted to cut costs. During the summer months, it is important to provide a shady area with adequate air circulation for the goats and to control flies.

Adequate space is essential for housing dairy goats to prevent aggressive does from monopolizing feed bunks and thus limiting the production of timid does. Each doe should have 15 square feet.

Feeders should be designed to discourage animals from wasting feed and to prevent feed from being contaminated with manure. Provide enough space for all animals to eat at one time. Outside, each doe should have at least 30 square feet of dry lot for exercise area if pasture is not available.

Basically, a goat house or shed must be built to provide shelter for the animals against the elements and from other animals. Goats prefer to stay in elevated places. Houses, therefore, must be provided with elevated sleeping areas. It must be well ventilated, well drained and easy to clean. Feeding racks should be provided. To give accessibility to both animals and the caretaker, flooring should be inclined by to facilitate drainage and cleaning.

Separate cages or housing should be provided for the lactating does, dry does, baby kids, and growing kids and the buck. The buck's cages must be placed far enough away, but still visible to the does.

A loafing area beside the goat houses must be provided (100 to 150 sq. M. per 50 head), complete with feeding racks and water troughs. This must be continuous along the goat house to allow them to loaf outside when preferred.

Any building material will do depending on finances and availability, but the flooring must always be cemented to facilitate the drying of the floor.

There are two main methods of housing dairy goats: (1) shed type or loose housing and (2) tie stalls or individual confinement. Some use a combination system, stalls for milking does and loose housing for the yearlings and kids.

LOOSE HOUSING

Also called Zero Pasture Management. This has many advantages and some disadvantages. These may be summarized as follows:

Advantages:

1. Exercise resulting from freedom is desirable.

2. Daily handling of manure is minimal or possibly eliminated, especially when slat floors are used.

3. Manure pack, when kept dry, provides heat and comfort.

Disadvantages:

1. Boss goats, especially when horned, may cause injury.

2. There will be much riding when a doe is in heat, thus using up energy.

The floor should be bedded regularly with dry straw, wood shavings or ground corn cobs to absorb moisture. Feeding stanchions serve as one side of the building. Stanchions permit one to control intake of feed.

Hay Stanchion

Goats are able to unlatch many types of latches, so must be secured properly.

**EUREKA!
I'VE OPENED IT**

Be sure to <u>lock</u> the grain supply!

CONFINEMENT HOUSING
This allows goats to be cared for so they do not become a nuisance by destroying gardens and trees.

Goats prefer high dry places.

BABY KID HOUSING

Open or partially open shed-type housing with raised wood slat-floored pens, off the floor at least fifteen inches provides dry draft-free quarters for kids. Pens should have three solid sides with the front side opening to the stall floor. Feeding, nursing and watering facilities should be placed outside the pen, accessible through keyholes for sanitation, necessary to prevent parasite and other disease problems caused or aided by contaminated feed. Bedding provided baby kids should be of inedible or unpalatable material such as sawdust, shavings, shredded straw, or sugar cane begasse. Pens for newborn kids should be provided with heat lamps in cold climates. These can be used until newborn kids are thoroughly dry and they have been given a few feedings of colostrum.

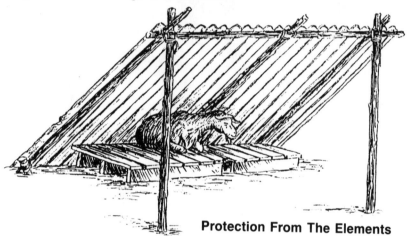

Protection From The Elements

THE IMPORTANCE OF WATER

Although not always considered as a nutrient, water is the largest single component of the animal body, comprising about 50 percent of the total body weight. Water is the fluid in which most body reactions take place. It is involved in cell structure, nutrient and waste transport, and the maintenance of body temperature.

Water is one of the most critical nutrients and should be supplied daily whenever possible. During lactation and hot weather, water should be available free choice. Some water is obtained from feed, some from body metabolism, but the largest intake is from drinking. The goat will drink water in amounts to about three times the weight of dry feed consumed. If the goat is grazing growing forage which contains about 75 percent water, it will drink less water directly. Extra water will be required in hot weather to cool the body.

The quantity and quality of drinking water will greatly influence the health and productivity of dairy goats. Milk is about 87 percent water, and milk production will be greatly reduced when water is in short supply. It is not necessary to heat or soften water for the use by animals. Excessive salt or salinity in water will reduce its intake and may affect the health of animals when it is consumed.

Proper sanitation is very important. Good sanitation is to be emphatically stressed if a group of goats, especially kids, are to be grouped together.

Fecal contamination of feed and water must be prevented. This means that feeders and waterers should be outside the pen whenever possible, and arranged so that fecal pellets cannot fall in. Grain should be put in Keyhole creep feeders, rather than at the open troughs that kids love to play and sleep in. Hay racks also, must be covered to keep kids out.

Because oocysts (of Coccidiosis-parasite disease), have to sporulate to develop into the infective stage of the disease, exposure can be reduced by cleaning the pens daily.

Slotted floors are helpful. Ordinary disinfectants don't destroy oocysts of Coccidiosis. It is important to concentrate on keeping the pens very dry, as moisture is necessary for sporulation, (development of Coccidiosisi.) Leaking waterers should be fixed at once, otherwise the wet ground or floor around the water source is a perfect environment for oocyst sporulation.

Small, grassy "exercise lots" are also very dangerous and should not be used. It is very important to over-crowding; spreading the kids out decreases the number of oocysts on any given square inch of pen floor or pasture. If many kids are present on the same farm, they should be grouped by age.

Putting a two week old innocent kid into a pen with kids two months old, where coccidial numbers and immunity have been building up for some time, is to invite disaster for the newcomer. Oocysts are killed by very cold temperatures, (far below 0°F-18°C or by hot dry conditions above 104°F or 40°C. Thus, at the end of the kidding season, pens and feeders should be moved out into the hot sunshine for natural sterilization.[2]

HERD SIRE HOUSING AND MANAGEMENT

The most important requirement for housing buck dairy goats is complete separation from the female members of the herd. Open shed housing with drop-down panels for summer weather is best. Bucks require only shelter from rain and a dry place to lie down. Several bucks can share the same area if at least 40 square feet, 12 M of pen space and 100 square feet, 30M of yard space is allotted for each. For housing one mature buck, the use of an open shed six feet by eight feet is adequate. The tethering arrangement allows the buck to exercise and at the same time keeps him under constant control.

Bucks with horns may be held by a collar. Hornless bucks should be held with a sturdy heavy leather halter. A simple open-fronted shade with a drop down panel on the rear wall for better summer ventilation will provide adequate shelter. Deep bedding should be used inside the shed.

BUCKS TOGETHER

It is dangerous to turn two mature bucks in together in the same pen suddenly. If raised together, it can be fairly safe if young, but if full grown, they still can be dangerous to each other.

A heavy utility pole guide wire should be stretched close to the surface of the ground between the building and an automobile axle driven its entire length into the ground at a point distant from the building. The length of wire can be as long as 200 feet, 60 M and the longer the better. A turnbuckle should be used on the wire to keep it stretched tightly. A small bull ring to which is attached a swivel and about 6 feet, 2 M of light chain should slide along the wire. If the tether wire is placed close to the ground surface, it is easy to mow the grass around and over it to keep the yard in good shape. The feeding facility provides for water, grain and hay feeding from the side away from access to the buck. This feeding facility should be placed so that the buck will have access to it but will not be able to move around it or get into it. Lengths of pipe keep the buck out of grain and water buckets and the hay rack is also made out of pipe to prevent the buck from chewing it. This buck housing arrangement is ideal for large fractious bucks. Opportunity for exercise and observation will keep bucks healthier and more contented.

FENCING

Goats are adventurous and are natural climbers, and efforts should be made to control them; the ultimate control would be high-tensile, electric fence. Goats stand and push on other fences and can be very destructive. Hazards that might contribute to broken legs and strangulations should be removed. Tethering goats is potentially dangerous since they are vulnerable to dog attacks, and if chained too close to another goat, invariably one will strangle. Goats chew on painted surfaces, and lead poisoning is a potential hazard in old barns. An efficient layout of pens, easy access to well-designed feeders and effective control will minimize management-related problems.

A five feet, 1.5 M high hog wire is one of the cheapest fencing available. Posts must be staked every two meters. Goats are fond of pounding their feet on the fences and scraping their bodies, so fences must be sturdily built.

It is virtually impossible to confine bucks with any other fence less than six feet, two meters high unless it is unclimbable. The doe should be taken to the buck pen for mating.

BEDDING

Inedible or unpalatable bedding is to be preferred over edible types. Sawdust, mill shavings, peanut hulls, shredded corn fodder, sugar cane bagasse, straw or poor quality hay are desirable forms. The drier the bedding material, the better.

1. Material for this chapter derived from Extension Goat Handbook, Extension Service. United States Department of Agriculture, March 1984, page B1-1.

2. M.C. Smith, Cornell University, Ithaea, N.Y.. Extension Goat Handbook, Extension Service U.S.D.A. G6-1984-page 2.

Section 10

Pasture Management

X. PASTURE MANAGEMENT[1,2]

GRASSES, FORBS, AND BROWSE

Goats do well on what they have, provided they are given the chance to choose. Although their nutrient requirements exceed those of most other livestock species, goats succeed while others fail. The reason for this success is that goats are particular. They consume the best parts only.

NUTRITIONAL VALUES OF GRASSES, FORBS, AND BROWSE PLANTS

Even though grasses are usually considered the most desirable type vegetation for livestock production, forbs, and browse plants (weeds and vines, shrubs, and trees) often contain higher levels of nutrients. Leguminous forbs and browse, for example, commonly contain more than 25 percent crude protein, whereas perennial grasses seldom exceed 15 per cent in crude protein content.

Browsing

THE GOAT AND DIET SELECTION

Goats are agile and have exaggerated control of their mouth parts, allowing them to be very selective for diet. They are able to stand on their hind legs and climb rock cliffs and low growing trees to gain access to relished plants and plant parts that are unavailable to other livestock species. Goats have a mobile upper lip, effective in nipping off plant parts very selectively. As a result, the goat's diet is very diversified, consisting of small components of a large number of plant species. Very simplified vegetation, an all-grass meadow, for example, does not provide good nutrition for goats over a long period of time. Goats need access to a wide variety of plants in order to exercise diet selection, as different plants increase and decrease in nutritional value with seasonal changes.

THE GOAT AS A BRUSH CONTROL TOOL

Many of the browse species have invaded or become overabundant in old, abandoned fields or on range and pasturelands following prolonged grazing by other livestock species. These invading species, collectively called "brush," often can be suppressed or eradicated using goats. Goats, especially the Angora breed are effective as brush control tools when the following requirements are met:

1. The brush is either low-growing or is reduced to low growth by mechanical means.

Grazing

2. The brush species is preferred by goats.

3. Goats can be concentrated in large numbers for a relatively short period, then removed for an extended period.

Each time the goats are concentrated, they consume the leaves and the twigs of the brush species, as well as a substantial portion of the grasses. When the goats are removed, the grasses recover more quickly than the brush. After several sequential grazings and rest periods, the brush is reduced to a density easily controllable, with a few goats included in the grazing herd. This method of brush control has proven successful in several regions of the United States, as well as at many locations around the World.

Goats will eat and destroy poison oak growth, so common in the hills of California, and their milk is not affected.

Summing up recommendations for use of pasture for goats: put young stock and dry stock on unimproved pastures and shrubby or weedy lots; they will make good use of this material. As long as they are not forced by starvation to eat poisonous plants, they will usually avoid them. Coarse, woody forage is excellent for young animals to develop good rumen function. After milking does have completed a lactation in which they were fed relatively large amounts of grain and highly digestible hay, browse of any kind is highly desirable to restore both rumen capacity and function to prepare them for the next lactation.

When goats are placed in improved pastures, they waste much more feed than they eat. It is much better to harvest the material daily and feed it to the herd in a feeder which will prevent the animals from contaminating the forage.

PASTURE MANAGEMENT

Permanent grass pastures are exceedingly difficult to manage for prevention of internal parasite problems. Rotation of animals using small areas which will furnish two-week periods of grazing is infinitely better than allowing animals continuous use of a large area. The individual areas can be managed using strip grazing with an electric fence. After animals are moved to a new area, the grazed area should be mown as short as possible and soil and grass stubble given full exposure to the sun. This effectively destroys worm larvae and provides new growth of fresh succulent forage for the next grazing period. The size and number of paddocks for grazing will be determined by the species of forage, the usual rainfall, and the number of animals. If pasture growth exceeds the need for grazing, nearly mature material can be removed for hay.

ANNUAL FORAGES

Use of annual grasses (piper sudan grass, annual brome grass, etc.), cow peas, and clovers are excellent means for furnishing goats palatable nutritious forage. Feeding them green forage results in much less waste than allowing the animals to graze. Comfrey, kudzu and other perennial forage crops can best be utilized by hand harvesting them and feeding them in fence line feeders. When feeding green forage and especially broad-leaved species such as comfrey, be cautious about feeding large amounts during times when the weather may interfere with normal growth of the plants. Periods of dark, cold, wet weather or periods of hot, dry weather may sufficiently alter the nitrate levels or produce other toxic nonprotein substances in the forage.

ZERO PASTURE MANAGEMENT

It is a program of confinement with goats, usually on elevated, slatted floors. Forage is brought to the goats. This is an improved way of caring for goats.

1. Extension Goat Handbook, U.S.D.A., pages b11 - 1 to 4.

2. *"Healthcare of the Goat and Sheep"*, R.A. Vanderhoof, VMD, 1987.

Section 11

Metabolic and Non-Infectious Diseases

XI. METABOLIC AND NON-INFECTIOUS DISEASES
(Malfunction of Body Processes)[1]

ANEMIA

Is a deficiency of circulating red blood cells thereby depriving body tissues of the proper amount of oxygen. Symptoms: Listlessness, weakness, lack of energy, blanched, whitened mucous membrane such as around the eye balls and the gums of the mouth. These should be a pink color when healthy.

Cause:
1. Internal parasites - attached to inside of stomach or intestines and sucking blood.
2. External parasites - attached to skin and some suck blood.
3. Severe hemorrhage - bleeding.
4. A blood disease - like anaplasmosis - destroys red blood cells.

ALLERGIES

Symptoms: Severe generalized symptoms such as sudden collapse, coma, and death may appear from allergies or insect stings. Less severe and more common symptoms may include respiratory distress (difficulty in breathing), heart irregularities, excessive saliva flow from the mouth or tears from the eyes, mild to severe itching, lumps (hives) that appear on the skin suddenly, hair standing erect, swelling of tissues with fluid retention (edema), and red areas on the skin.

Cause/Transmission: An allergy is the reaction to a substance (usually a protein) with which it has had previous contact and to which the body has developed an immune sensitivity. Many substances can cause allergic reactions with varying degrees of severity. Common causes of allergies are feeds, infection, applications of certain chemicals to the skin, and insect bites. Some examples are pollens or other plant proteins, insect stings, many drugs and biological substances such as antisera, vaccines, or antibiotics. Many times the allergic reaction is dose related: small doses cause small reactions and large doses cause severe shock or even death. These reactions can occur almost immediately after contact or up to 3 weeks later.

Treatment: Immediately remove the animal from its surroundings because the allergen usually is nearby. If the suspected allergen was applied to the skin, wash the animal with soap and water. (Protect yourself from the suspected allergen). Doses of antihistamines and corticosteroids injected or taken orally, Methylprednisolone acetate (cortico-steroid) and Chlorpheniramine maleate (antihistamine) usually produce a dramatic response, completely reversing or greatly reducing the severity of the allergy. To prevent further recurrence, do not place the animal in the same environment or use the same products.

BLOAT

Is gas forming in the rumen from overeating lush clover-type pasture or grain.

Treatment: Fashion a wooden bit, e.g., piece of a broom handle; attach a cord or leather strap from each end back around head. Place in mouth crosswise like a horse bit so that animal will fight it with mouth and tongue. Then hold animal upright and shake or dance him up and down.

COLOSTRUM

Because the doe's first milk, called colostrum, is high in antibody level, it is very important for the kid to nurse soon after birth. It should receive about 10% of its body weight in colostrum the first day of life. This would amount to nearly 236 ml (½ pint) for the average-sized kid.

GOITER

Cause: A lack of iodine in the diet — in iodine deficient areas of the world.

Symptoms: Swollen area on neck under the chin.

Treatment: Supply an adequate iodine preparation in the food.

Note: See page 47 for illustration of Goiter.

POLIOENCEPHALOMALACIA

Usually a brain disturbance from bad feed. No treatment is available. But Vitamin B_1 (Thiamin hydrochloride) can be injected I.M. or S.C. for possible improvement. Use 1 cc daily for several days, adult goat. General treatment: Inject Bo-SE into any sick animal - ½ to 2½ cc to adults.

PREGNANCY TOXEMIA[2]

("Twin lambing disease" in sheep), Ketosis, Acetonemia. A major killer of goats. Too much fat being "burned" in body and not enough carbohydrates in the diet.

Associated often with:

1. Multiple fetuses and fat animals.
2. Under or overfeeding - late pregnancy stress.
3. Lack of exercise.
4. Occurs during last 40 days of pregnancy.
5. Real fat does will sometimes stop eating.
6. Sometimes neurological signs occur:

a. Appear to be blind, "propping" against any kind of obstruction.

b. Often hold head in an "S" curve, muscles twitching around eyes and ears, etc.

c. Severe depression, listlessness, grinding of teeth.

d. Urine will be positive for ketosis, (acetonemia).

Test for Pregnancy Toxemia: Use special acetonemia test strips to check a urine sample from a doe with any of the above symptoms.

7. Advanced states: paralysis, abortion, finally death. There is about 50% mortality, even with treatment.

Prevention:

1. Avoid stress of any kind, e.g., storms, transport, feed interruptions, etc.
2. Obesity should be avoided in early pregnancy.
3. An adequate and good food supply during the last 6 weeks of pregnancy. If pasture becomes poor, heavier feeding may become necessary.
4. Early cases can be identified by gentle driving of the whole flock - the slower ones being separated out and given special care and nourishment.
5. Do not allow any interruption in feed intake.
6. In overly fat, pregnant does, gentle driving for 20 to 30 minutes per day may prevent incipient cases from developing, by elevating the blood glucose.
7. Prevent overeating of grains.
8. During the last 40 days of pregnancy, start adding molasses or brown sugar to the ration in small amounts at first. Then increase to about ½ of ration.

Treatment: Only successful in early stages of disease.

1. 10% glucose solution IV, generic products.
2. Propylene glycol, generic products. Give 4 ounces (120 ml) twice daily by mouth.

1. Material derived from *Healthcare of the Goat and Sheep*, R.A. Vanderhoof, VMD, 1987.

2. The Merck Veterinary Manual, 7th edition, page 456, "Pregnancy Toxemia in Ewes", which also applies to Does.

Section 12

Infectious and Contagious Diseases

XII. Infectious and Contagious Diseases[12]

ANAPLASMOSIS

Symptoms: Anemia is the most common symptom. Anemic animals have poor, emaciated appearance and do not milk or reproduce well.

Cause/Transmission: This blood parasitic disease of goats is caused by the rickettsia Anaplasma ovis. The disease is usually passed from animal to animal by infected ticks, bloodsucking flies, and blood-contaminated needles and surgical instruments. Infected animals that show no symptoms of the disease are carriers of the organism. The disease is fairly common in areas where anaplasmosis occurs in cattle.

Diagnosis requires a laboratory examination to detect the organism inside the red blood cells.

Treatment/Prevention: Tetracycline drugs are recommended for prevention and treatment. Suggested treatment is based on cattle-dosage control at 4 mg/kg body weight intramuscularly, 4 times at 3 day intervals with the 200 mg/ml oxytetracycline, "Liquamycin 200" - Pfizer, or administered orally in feed at 20 to 30 mg per head per day on a continuing basis. Control of flies and ticks will help, as will sanitation of instruments used for castration, etc. Severe stress also tends to increase the risk of an anaplasmosis outbreak.

BABESIOSIS

Symptoms: Goats usually show no outward clinical signs of Babesia infection.

Diagnosis: same as for Anaplasmosis.

Prevention: Control and prevention are based on controlling ticks with dips or sprays. See Chapter XV for illustration on dipping and spraying.

BRUCELLOSIS

This disease in goats is known as Malta Fever, caused by Brucella melitensis.

Symptoms:

1. Does may abort in final 4-6 weeks of pregnancy. Severe placentitis (inflammation of the afterbirth tissue).

2. Males may have swollen joints and testicles.

3. The germ is shed in the urine, milk, and vaginal discharge for 2 to 3 months, and can cause infection in people (undulant fever) and, or Malta fever.

Warning: Do not use the "Strain 19" vaccine that is used for cattle on goats as there is danger of giving them the disease.

CAE (Caprine Arthritis Encephalitis)

A viral contagious disease of goats of all breeds, ages and sexes. CAE causes encephalitis (brain symptoms) in the young goats and arthritis (inflammation of the joints) in the adults. It is transmitted from the infected doe to the kid through the colostrum (first milk). There is no treatment or vaccine at present. The only prevention is pasteurization of the colostrum. See under "Mycoplasma". CAE is usually not seen in meat goats.

CASEOUS LYMPHADENITIS - "CL" - (abscesses), (boils)

Probably the most common ailment in goats. **Cause**: a bacteria.

Symptoms and Treatment: Swelling on the body, usually around the neck that will turn into abscesses and will rupture unless lanced. If they are opened surgically, which should be done, the resulting pus should be caught in a rag or paper and burned to prevent premise contamination. The abscesses should be flushed out with hydrogen peroxide or Betadine (a "tamed" iodine preparation) and left open to heal.

Prevention: There is no vaccine and the injection of antibiotics, like penicillin does not have much effect. Keep animals that are under treatment - isolated from the flock for about 2 weeks until wounds completely heal.

CHLAMYDIAL DISEASE

An abortion producing disease caused by a very small bacteria.

CONTAGIOUS AGALACTIA (MYCOPLASMA) AND ARTHRITIS

Cause/Transmission: Contagious agalactia is a disease of goats caused by mycoplasma agalactia. The organism is found in milk, urine, feces, and eye and nasal fluids for several months after infection. Spreading may occur when an uninfected goat contacts these secretions.

Treatment/Prevention: Helpful antibiotics are Tetracycline or Tylosin, (Tylosin dosage: 1 ml. of the 200 mg. product per 50 lbs. body weight (or 22.7 kg body weight), given intramuscularly. **(Liquamycin)** - LA-200 - 3 to 5 mg. per lb. of body weight given daily. (1/2 kg) im, continue injections 24 to 48 hours after improvement is noted. The death rate can reach 20% of the infected animals. A vaccine is available in some countries.

CONTAGIOUS CAPRINE PLEUROPNEUMONIA

Cause/Transmission: Contagious caprine pleuropneumonia is caused by Mycoplasma sp. and is commonly seen in Africa, Asia, the Mediterranean, and has been reported in Mexico. The disease is spread by contact with an infected animal.

Treatment/Prevention: Same as for contagious agalactia.

CONTAGIOUS ECTHYMA - (SORE MOUTH) — "CE" (Orf)

Disease of sheep and goats, worse in goats, caused by a virus highly resistant to drying. Virus has remained viable for at least 12 years on premises of an outbreak, and is worldwide.

Symptoms: Incubation of 2 to 3 days. Papules then vesicles then pustules then scabs.

1. Small blisters on lips and gums, eyelids, nostrils, tongue, and palate, raised proliferative tissue under scabs.

2. Rupture and form scabs over inflamed, raised areas.

3. Kids - lesions develop on gums of incisor teeth and then refuse to nurse, but when they do they spread infection to teats of does, producing:

   a. infection in doe and up teat canal - mastitis.

   b. lesions on feet and genitals of bucks and does.

   c. unthrifty condition and slow growth.

4. Most common in August, September and October.

Transmission: goats and sheep should not be exhibited in fairs, sales, and shows if there is a chance of exposing other animals.

Immunity: Goats that have an attack are highly immune thereafter.

Prevention: A vaccine is available, but should not be used if there is no history of the disease on the premises. If one starts using, must vaccinate all newcomers to premises. Adults are usually immune for 5 years after vaccination.

Treatment: The scabby material is removed, then treat wounds with hydrogen peroxide or chlorhexidine.

Precaution: This disease serves as a good example why there should be veterinary inspection and clearance or rejection prior to all shows and fairs. In vaccination and treating lesions, rubber or plastic gloves should be worn. Humans can become infected, producing very painful lesions, inflammation of hands and auxiliary lymph nodes, persisting for weeks.

ENTEROTOXEMIA - OVEREATING DISEASE

It causes sudden death. **Cause**: Overeating - too much grain.

Prevention: Vaccination 3 to 4 weeks of age and then boostered at 6 to 7 weeks then again at 6 months. Revaccinate adults every 6 months. Use Clostridium perfringens Type C and D vaccine. Prevent animals from overeating.

EYE INFECTIONS - PINKEYE

Cause: A bacteria.

Transmission: Dusty conditions. Flying insects.

Treatment: Antibiotic ointments, such as Terramycin or Chloromycetin ointment or Tylan eye powder.

Prevention: There is now a vaccine available. Protect from flies.

FOOT AND MOUTH DISEASE (APHTHOUS FEVER)

Symptoms: Symptoms of foot and mouth disease in goats are usually less severe than those seen in cattle. Goat symptoms include dullness, fever and small blisters on the mouth and tongue that break and leave small pits. Small blisters also will appear between the toes and on the feet. These areas turn pale and then peel off, leaving erosions and sores between the toes. The affected animals are very lame. The same type of blisters and erosions appear on the teats. Affected animals will not eat, and if the feet are very sore, will not stand. Sometimes the first symptoms are sudden death in kids, with abortions in the adults. Ministries and Departments of Agriculture require that FMD be reported, if suspected. Diagnosis is based on symptoms and laboratory confirmations. The disease should be differentiated from goat pox, and contagious ecthyma.

Cause/Transmission: Foot and mouth disease is caused by a virus that has seven types and over 60 subtypes. It is widespread over much of the world. The disease is spread by swallowing the virus on feed or by inhaling or getting virus particles in the eyes from virus-laden air. Spread by recovered carrier cattle, sheep, goats, and hogs, foot and mouth disease can occur for a year or longer after the symptoms are gone. There is some evidence the virus can be spread through the air by winds.

Treatment and Prevention: There is no effective treatment. Vaccination can be made as a preventive measure against the type that occurs locally. Some countries use the eradication method - all exposed and sick animals are destroyed, then burned, or buried.

FOOT ROT

Cause: Two bacteria working together.

Transmission: Wet, soggy ground or damp manure-filled areas.

Prevention: A vaccine is available. Wellcome Labs.

Treatment: Antibiotic injections. Close, deep, and severe hoof trimming. Foot baths. Zinc Sulphate solution and copper sulfate solution. This malady will be addressed in more detail in this text. See Chapter XVII.

HEARTWATER DISEASE[3]

An infectious, noncontagious disease of ruminants found in areas infested by ticks of the genus Amblyomma: regions of Africa, and the islands of Madagascar, Reunion, Mauritius and Caribbean.

Symptoms: High Fever
Tear formation
Convulsions
Loss of appetite
Exaggerated blinking of eyes
Chewing movements
Prostration

Prevention and Treatment:
Control tick infestation
Tetracyclines at 10 to 20 mg/kg of body wt.
A second and third treatment may be necessary.

MELIODOSIS[4]

Cause/Transmission: Caused by the bacterium Pseudomonas pseudomallei, meliodosis is most commonly seen in South East Asia, but also occurs in most other areas of the world. Infection is due to the contamination of wounds with soil containing the organism. Spread from animal to animal or animal to man is unlikely.

Treatment and Prevention: Older animals sometimes recover but may get sick again when under stress. If you do decide to treat, use tetracycline, chloramphenicol, or sulfa drugs. No vaccine is available. As a precaution, healthy animals should be kept away from areas where the disease has occurred.

Human Health Concerns: Although unlikely, human infection may occur as a result of swallowing the organism. Parts or products from infected animals should not be used for human food unless the animal recovers completely.

MYCOPLASMA

Cause: A very small bacteria that can cause the following diseases and is spread through colostrum (the first milk): Pneumonia, Mastitis - (inflammation of the udder), Polyarthritis - (more than one joint affected with inflammation), Abortion - (birth before term), usually dead, pinkeye, diseases of the central nervous system (spinal cord and brain). Two of the above that are probably most devastating to the goat owner are mastitis and abortions.

Prevention: Pasteurization of the colostrum and giving to the newborn before they nurse the doe. Colostrum is pasteurized at 131 degrees F (56 degrees C) for 1 hour. If the temperature varies 1 or 2 degrees below, the mycoplasma will not be killed and if above 131 degrees the colostrum will be ruined.

Treatment: Culling the affected animals. There is no vaccine.

NAVEL ILL

Cause: Filthy premises. Contamination of the umbilicus (navel cord) at birth or shortly afterwards - from unsanitary kidding quarters.

Symptoms: Infection and pus in the joints; acute lameness; internal abcesses; retarded development.

Prevention: Good management. Clean kidding premises. Soak the umbilical (navel) stump with Tincture of Iodine 7%, just once. Inspect the umbilicus in 4 to 5 days for signs of infection.

Treatment: Wide spectrum antibiotics, like penicillin, streptomycin, Oxytetracycline injected IM. About 5 ml daily for 1 week.

PESTE DES PETIT RUMINANTS[5]

Cause: The disease is caused by a virus and has been reported only in West Africa.

Transmission: By direct contact with sick animals or with areas where sick animals have been recently kept. All tissues and fluids from sick animals contain the virus and are considered infectious.

Symptoms: A sudden rise in temperature, up to 106 degrees F (41 degrees C), is seen in goats that appear dull and restless. They have a dull coat, a dry muzzle with a clear discharge, very little appetite, and reddening around the eyes. There may be some red or raw areas in the mouth. Diarrhea, dehydration, emaciation and collapse sometimes occur. Pneumonia may develop as a complication. Most infected goats die within 8 to 10 days.

Several other diseases have similar symptoms, thus laboratory diagnosis should be made using blood and culture tests. It has been reported to 10 to 90% fatal in goats.

Treatment/Prevention: There is no effective treatment. A vaccine that will protect sheep and goats for about 1 year is available in some areas.

RABIES - (HYDROPHOBIA)

A rare but always fatal viral infection conferred by a bite and saliva from an infected animal.

Symptoms: Excitation, depression, paralysis, coma and death.

Prevention: A relatively new and improved rabies vaccine that can be used on all classes of livestock. There is a new and improved vaccine for humans, also.

RESPIRATORY DISEASE (Lungs and upper and lower air passages).

Cause: Stress from
1. Overcrowding - excess dust.
2. Chilling - sudden temperature changes, especially newborn kids.
3. Weaning.
4. Long distance hauling. "Shipping fever"
5. Poorly ventilated barns.
6. Malnutrition.
7. Feed changes.
8. Parasitism.
9. Worming.

Symptoms:
1. Nasal Discharge.
2. Anorexia, (reduced appetite), weight loss.
3. Accelerated breathing and heart rate.
4. Fever.
5. Depression.

6. Coughing.
7. Reluctance to move.
8. Paleness or anemic.
9. Cyanosis of mucous membrane. (Turning blue).
10. Gray-blue lymph nodes.
11. Finally, shock and then death.

Treatment of respiratory disease:
1. Treat early in course of disease and for sufficient length of time.
2. Use the appropriate antibiotic drug given in adequate doses, (eg., Ampicillin, Naxel, Nuflor, Tylosin, Oxytetracycline).
3. Use the most suitable antibiotic. Include a sulfa drug, e.g., Sulfamethazine (use simultaneously with antibiotics, such as Tylosin). Some are available for drinking water.

In general, medications should be continued for 3 days after temperature is normal.

Separate sick animals from the healthy. Isolate recently shipped or hauled animals for 2 to 3 weeks so sick animals can be treated early. Careful nursing of the young should not be overlooked.

Adequate colostrum should be given to the newly born. A colostrum bank should be maintained. Milk cartons make handy containers, in which colostrum can be kept frozen until ready for use.

Overcrowding should be avoided. Need 14 square feet per pregnant animal, including following birth.

RIFT VALLEY FEVER[6]

Cause: Goats are affected by this virus - caused disease transmitted primarily by mosquitoes. Ticks have also been identified as carriers. The disease is seen primarily on the African continent usually during the wet season.

Symptoms: High abortion rate occurs in adults and high death losses among very young animals. Sick animals show a rapid rise in temperature and a rapid, weak pulse. Gait is unsteady. Sores sometimes appear on the tongue and cheeks. Milk production rapidly decreases. Death losses are extremely high for young lambs, kids, calves, and puppies. Adult goats suffer a 10 to 20% death loss.

Treatment/Prevention: There is no effective treatment. Prevention consists of housing animals in insect-proof buildings or moving them to highlands away from insects. A vaccine is available; however, it is a live-virus vaccine and will cause abortions in pregnant animals and deformities in the fetus.

Human Health Concerns: Humans are infected both by carrier insects and by handling animals and tissues affected with this virus. Meat from infected animals should not be eaten. In humans, the disease is not usually fatal but does cause a long, 7 to 10 day flu-like disease that is very debilitating and painful. A vaccine is available for use in humans.

SALMONELLOSIS DYSENTERY

An acute contagious disease of goats, not uncommon. Two forms, enteric and abortion. Death rate severe in spite of vigorous treatment. Triggered often by high stress factors.

Diagnosis: Difficult because symptoms are similar to other diseases.
1. Severe watery black or bloody scours with putrid odor.
2. Mortality very high in young kids.
3. Normally does not occur with older animals unless stressed, e.g., transportation or temporary feed reduction or passage through a sales barn or auction market.
4. Abortion.

Prevention: These are only effective means of control
1. Strict sanitation.
2. Avoid management changes.
3. Recovered animals often become chronic carriers for many months and serve as a source of infection to others.

Treatment:
1. Only effective if started early in course of disease.
2. Administer large quantities of electrolytes, e.g., Gatorade orally, or human oral rehydration fluids
3. Administer large doses of broad spectrum antibiotics, e.g., Oxytetracycline 2cc, IM twice daily for 7 to 10 days.

TETANUS - LOCKJAW

Cause: An anaerobic bacteria (one that cannot live in the presence of oxygen). This bacteria produces a toxin (poison) that attacks the nervous system and eventually the brain. This disease is easy to prevent but difficult to cure. The bacteria are found everywhere, the world over, and especially in the manure of animals.

Symptoms: Usually are produced in 10 days after infection.
1. Muscle spasms, convulsions.
2. Head thrown back and legs stretched out rigid.
3. Death, in 3 to 10 days.

Mode of Contamination:
1. Castration (especially by elastrators which are heavy rubber bands that are applied above the testicles).
2. Wounds produced by shearing, disbudding, dehorning, tail docking, or any wound.
3. Untreated navel cord.

Treatment: Not very satisfactory.
1. If early enough in course of the disease, the wound can be debrided (cleaned surgically) and packed with gauze soaked with antibiotic.

2. Antibiotics, systemically e.g., Penicillin-Streptomycin, SQ or IM or IV.

Prevention: Very satisfactory, using two types of vaccines.
1. Immediate protection by inoculating with tetanus antitoxin which lasts for 2 weeks.
2. Protection for about 1 year after vaccination with **tetanus toxoid**. About a 9 day period is required to build up immunity.
3. Use these two at time of surgical procedure. Both kinds can be given intramuscularly or subcutaneously simultaneously.
4. There is a vaccine available that has both Clostridium perfringens type C and D, and **tetanus toxoid**, all in one.
5. When using the **tetanus toxoid**, a booster inoculation should be given about 45 to 60 days following the initial vaccination, then give an annual booster thereafter.
6. Employ clean techniques on the animal and disinfect the instruments when doing any surgical procedure.
7. Keep animal quarters clean and free of wire, broken glass, nails in boards, etc.

TICK-BORNE FEVER[7]

It is also called Tick-Borne Encephalitis. It is caused by a virus, and affects goats, sheep and cattle as well as rodents. It is found in European countries and is carried by a tick, Ioxides ricinus. It can also be transmitted through milk.

Symptoms: Fever, weight and growth loss, dullness, loss of appetite, and abortions. These symptoms last from 5 to 8 days, then the animal is usually recovered. Although they remain immune from the disease themselves, they will be carriers the rest of their lives.

Prevention: Control tick infestation. Keep animals in tick-free pastures and/or dip them with an ascaricide (preparation, eg. Co-Ral to kill ticks.)

Treatment: Oxytetracycline (Liquamycin 200) and Sulfamethazine.

TUMORS

The goat is not especially prone to tumors - both benign and malignant being quite rare. However, about 1% of the Angora goat population does have skin cancer - usually in the form of pedunculated (hanging) growths on the side of the vulva or under the tail.

Skin warts are known to affect the Saanen breed of milk goats occasionally. Wart growths are found mainly on milking goats that are whiter in color than others, and nearly all parts of the body are affected. Often these growths will develop into malignant tumors.

Some tumors can be removed surgically by a veterinarian.

1. Extension Goat Handbook, USDA.
2. *"Healthcare of the Goat and Sheep"*, R.A. Vanderhoof, VMD, 1987.
3. The Merck Veterinary Manual, 7th Edition, page 396, Heartwater Disease.
4. Ibid, Page 360-Meliolosis.
5. Ibid, page 402, Peste De Petits.
6. Ibid, page 403, Rift Valley Fever.
7. Ibid, page 405, Tick-Borne Fever.

Section 13

Reproduction

XIII. REPRODUCTION[1]

Goats are considered short-day breeders - estrus (heat) is brought on and increases with the decreasing light of shorter days. Estrus does are usually mated with bucks at onset of estrus and then at 12 hour intervals until heat subsides. The most fertile period for bucks and does in the northern hemisphere is late August through January.

In the Northern Hemisphere, most goats cycle during October, November, December, and January. They may fail to come in heat until the winter solstice (December 21), but some does cycle until March 1. There is breed variation and much individual variation as to when they start cycling. Individual variation is greater than breed variation.

The length between the caprine (goat) estrus cycles is 18 to 24 days. Nubians tend to have the longest cycles, often extending from July to March.

The duration of estrus is 24 to 96 hours, but average is 40 hours. Standing heat is usually 12 to 24 hours, but can be as short as a few hours.

Goats near the equator cycle year round, and two kid crops a year are possible. In temperature latitudes they are seasonally polyestrous (having more than one heat). Silent heats (not noticeable) are common at the beginning and end of the season. Decreasing light and temperature helps to bring a doe into heat. The introduction of a buck or its smell at the beginning of the season will often bring the whole group into heat, in an average of 8 days. Most goats will eventually cycle even without the buck's presence. A doe occasionally shows heat when she is already pregnant, but rarely will goats come into estrus after being bred (successfully). Gestation is 150 days, with a variation of 145 to 155 days.

Signs of estrus include:

1. Swelling and redness of the vulva, followed by a clear discharge which becomes white by the end of the estrus.
2. Uneasiness.
3. Tail switching.
4. Continuous bleating.
5. Frequent urination.
6. Riding and standing with other does are less common than with cows. A doe that is not in heat will resist pressure on her lower back and attempts to grab her tail. The doe should be bred the last half of estrus. General advice is to breed the second day and repeat in 12 hours if she is still in heat. The does' milk production will decrease during estrus, and she should be segregated from the herd to maintain tranquility. If the doe fails to show strong heat, one trick to try is to rub a rag on a buck's head, to accumulate his odor, then

keep the rag in a covered jar, and offer it to the doe once a day. When in heat, she will follow the jar all over the barn. In cold weather, the buck jar may need to be heated to improve its aroma.

Although goats come into heat when they are about 3 to 4 months old, a doe should be 7 to 10 months old, or better yet, 80 to 90 pounds before breeding. Underweight doelings are often anestrous (without heat) or have silent heats. If they do become pregnant, they will produce fewer kids than the average well-grown doe. Fertility and twinning can be increased by flushing (increasing energy feed, not protein) for two weeks before breeding. Also, statistically more kids result from breeding on the second heat of the season than the first.

Rectal temperature regarding kidding: For about a week before kidding, the doe's temperature will be above normal, about 103 degrees or above, but approximately 24 hours before birth it falls below normal. This can be very useful.

Dehorned and descented bucks are not as efficient breeders. Most does will ovulate by the 10th day after introduction of the buck. A thin clear mucous discharge becomes thicker after ovulation.

FALSE PREGNANCY

It is also called pseudopregnancy or pseudocyesis, or cloudburst. The goat is the only ruminant that has this condition. It is fairly common and usually occurs following breeding. It is also common in anestrus or non-pregnant does. Some even come into lactation. The condition is a hydrometra (water in the uterus) and usually terminates at the doe's approximate due date, with "delivery" of a large volume of cloudy fluid. In about 50 percent of these does, subsequent pregnancies are normal.

Treatment: The use of prostaglandins such as Lutylase or Estrumate, (only available from a licensed Veterinarian), can be used to terminate pseudopregnancy.

RETAINED PLACENTAS (after birth = fetal membranes), R.P.

Placentas normally drop quite rapidly after parturition (birth) in several hours. If retained after 12 hours, one should get a little concerned.

Treatment: Leave the R.P. alone. Give an antibiotic parenteral (IM. or SC.) to combat toxicity in the doe and the possible development of laminitis (founder - feet become engorged with blood and very painful). Does will sometimes contract tetanus from an R.P., so protect with tetanus antitoxin. R.P. should normally fall out in 2 to 3 days.

Prevention: Bo-Se injected intramuscularly several times through the year.

BUCK EVALUATION FOR BREEDING AND SOUNDNESS
1. Examine for general or total health.
2. Their structural (anatomical) soundness - locomotion.
3. Teeth.

4. Feet - should be trimmed if necessary.

5. Examine reproductive apparatus - penis, prepuce, and testicles.

a) Palpate (feel) testicles for size, e.g., 30 centimeters total circumference should be a minimum. Also check for consistency and symmetry. (The two halves should be approximately the same size.)

b) Spermatogenesis (ability to produce sperm) is highly correlated with testicle weight and size, therefore, 35 to 38 cm. circumference would be better.

c) Bucks are rendered sterile or partially sterile for about a 60 day period after sickness, fever, or transportation.

6. Small testicles (30 cm. down to 25 cm. should be culled) that are soft, small, or hardened and asymmetrical (different size). The epididymis (the cord leading from top to bottom of testicle) can and should be palpated for possible swelling and inflammation.

7. Stress - shipping, high temperatures, or sickness will affect breeding efficiency. Sperm cycle of formation in testicle is about 50 days, and 11 to 15 for sperm to pass up into tract, about 60 days total.

8. Semen evaluation by microscopic examination of spermatozoa.

9. A mature buck can service 30 to 40 females if the breeding season is evenly spread from August through March, and if not more than two does are to be serviced per day.

10. A buck kid starts pestering the does at 8 weeks of age. By three months he may serve does that he can mount and reach, but not until 6 or more months can he inseminate them. It is advised to separate young bucks from young females.

11. The young buck should not be pressed into full service until the second breeding season.

12. Do not allow him to run with the herd. He can be dangerous, vicious and will attack you.

13. Any doe in heat may be serviced, 5, 10, or 20 times. This is a waste of energy for the buck and may be physically harmful for the doe. A doe too young to be bred may become pregnant.

14. The buck should be in a pen with an exercise area located 200 feet away from the does and the fence should be at least 6 feet high.

15. Fecal examination for internal parasites by use of a magnifying glass, or microscope to detect the eggs of worms.

MULTIPLE BIRTHS

The usual or average number of kids per parturition (birth) is two, but often have three or not uncommon to have four, occasionally five. A herd of 30 does or more kidding should produce 200%.

ARTIFICIAL INSEMINATION (placing semen directly into uterus)

The doe is inseminated 1 to 12 hours after onset of estrus (heat).

REPRODUCTIVE FAILURES

There are many known and unknown reasons for reproductive failures in the doe. Some of these are as follows:

1. Infertile sperm from the buck.

2. Abnormal egg from the doe.

3. Hormone malfunction such as retained corpus luteum - (yellow body), located on the ovary and produces a hormone that prevents abortion.

4. Overfat condition of doe can prevent conception (pregnancy).

5. Cyst(s) on the ovary.

6. Very hot weather may prevent conception or cause the fertilized egg to be aborted (die and pass out of the body).

7. In isolated cases, malnutrition (improper feeding) or lack of protein, deficiency of the mineral phophorous and the lack of vitamin A can prevent normal reproduction and cause abortion.

8. A normal fetus may be aborted due to the female being injured by other animals or being bumped in a narrow door opening.

BREEDING

Buck kids should be separated from doelings at 3 months of age. Bucks are old enough for light service at 6 to 12 months.

Bucks should not be used for extensive or heavy service until 18 months of age.

Bucks should not be left to run in the same pen as does. Bucks will worry does resulting in reduction of milk and buck odor may taint the milk.

Both sexes will breed better if they are gaining in condition or weight after being thin. Nubians, especially, tend to get fat during their dry season. Fat goats have more trouble getting bred and also with difficult or abnormal birth. Sixty days after kidding, the doe is bred. Breeding is repeated 12 hours later. Ninety days after breeding, stop milking the doe. Sixty days later, the doe will give birth again. Using this system of breeding, the does will kid at least twice a year. Purebred does will average three kids per year.

Artificial insemination (A.I) with frozen semen is being utilized to rapidly improve genetics where no bucks are available. It can be used to provide a variable source of outside genetics to prevent inbreeding, as well as to crossbred to take advantage of hybrid vigor or to gradually build an improved breeding herd. It is, many times, easier and cheaper to transport semen from improved bucks than to transport and house live animals. Acquire semen only from a reputable supplier with a proven disease control program in effect. It requires a well trained technician with the proper semen storage and insemination equipment, careful doe management and excellent record keeping in order to be successful.

PARTURITION
Signs of Approaching Kidding
1. Uneasiness and restlessness.
2. Lying down and getting up.
3. Pawing and bedding.
4. Bleating.
5. A mucous discharge will soil the tail and genital area.
6. The water bag may be visible.

WHEN TO BREED	TIMING GUIDE FOR DAIRY GOATS		
Doe comes into heat	Doe in full standing heat	Doe at end of heat	
	30 hrs	Egg Released	
0 hrs Early Heat	24 hrs Standing Heat	36 hrs late Heat	48 hrs
too early	Good	Best Timing	Good	Too Late

KIDDING DOES
1. Provide adequate exercise for the doe right up to kidding.
2. Feed additional grain during last month of pregnancy.
3. Confine the doe to the maternity pen prior to kidding.
   a) The maternity pen should be clean and freshly bedded.

b) Clean the doe before putting her in the pen. The long hairs around the hind limbs, perineum (area under the tail), and udder should be clipped to make clean-up easier after kidding.

c) Don't put water bucket in kidding pen. Other does may push kids into water and they may drown.

Attendance at kidding is life saving and cleanliness is very important. The fetus acquires the capacity of extrauterine life only shortly before term, and may die in utero if parturition is unduly delayed. As kidding time approaches, the udder rapidly enlarges, the pelvic ligaments relax around the tail head, and the vulva becomes greatly enlarged. Eight to twelve hours before birth, the cervix begins to dilate and the cervical mucus plug will be in evidence, as a tan, sticky substance smeared about the hind parts of the doe. This first stage of kidding lasts 1 to 6 hours. If progress stops, a vaginal exam with clean, well-lubricated hands is in order.

Normally the fetus enters the birth canal and the doe starts an abdominal press. The chorioallantoic sac is ruptured and the unbroken amniotic sac (water bag) is then forced through the vulva. Delivery of the kids usually occurs in a short time once the water bag can be viewed. Kids may be presented either with their front feet forward (normal), or in posterior presentation where their rear feet are presented first. The doe may rest between each kid for a short period of time. Most does are best left alone during parturition. Interference with parturition of does kidding for the first time may result in the doe rejecting the kids. It is important that does lick the kids as soon as possible after they are born as this indicates her acceptance of them. Dystocias (difficult births) are rarely encountered.

If labor is prolonged for more than one hour with no progress, a vaginal exam is again indicated. With multiple births, more than one fetus may be lodged in the pelvis. Careful sorting is necessary before delivery is possible. The goat's uterus is very fragile and prolonged manipulation may result in uterine rupture. "Ring womb" occurs, when, with prolonged labor, the cervix begins to contract, making delivery impossible. Caesarean sections are done with overlarge fetuses, monsters, malformed "Ring womb" and other dystocia that might threaten the doe's life.

After parturition, the doe should begin to lick the kids, and she may eat part of the fetal membranes. There is no evidence for benefit or harm from ingestion of the fetal membranes. Normal kids will start trying to stand up immediately and should be on their feet and nursing within a short period of time. It is important that kids nurse the doe as soon as possible after birth in order to get the first milk or colostrum. It may be necessary occasionally to help weak kids to nurse. Kids' navels should be dipped in iodine solution. Retention of the fetal membranes, a condition not uncommon in cows, seldom occurs in goats. The placenta is discharged naturally 3-5 days if not normally expelled within 6 hours after kidding. Systemic antibiotics are indicated only if the doe shows signs of illness.

Thorough disinfection of pens after each delivery and especially after any problems is important for successful reproductive management. Colostrum feeding should be continued to kids beyond the first hours after kidding for three days. Excess colostrum can be frozen successfully for later use in the kiddings. The fresh doe will normally discharge a deep red, mucus-like material called lochia for 7 to 14 days postpartum. Abnormal is a large amount of bright red blood, foul-smelling exudate, or pus.

a) Know when to assist or seek the advice of a knowledgeable person.

b) Does assisted in birth when the uterus is entered by hand should be treated with intrauterine antibiotics. A sulfa bolus or pill placed in the uterus, after parturition process is completed is necessary.

KID CARE AT PARTURITION
1. The kid born during a normal parturition seldom needs human help to survive.

2. Kids born during dystocias or difficult birth may need help. The most important thing is to clear the mucus out of the mouth and start the kid breathing. Hold the kid by the back feet with head down and swing and shake to clear throat of mucus. Touch, tickle, or pinch the nose to provoke sneezing. Pinch hard on the skin between the toes or on the ears or the tail. This will usually make a kid scream and in order to scream, it must breathe in first. A kid which is not breathing well, will not inflate its lungs properly and will be a candidate for pneumonia.

3. Assist the doe in cleaning and drying kids that are to be dam raised; or remove bottle fed kids immediately after birth and towel them dry. They don't really need a heat lamp other than just drying off the kid.

4. Remove the placenta (afterbirth) and discharges as they are expelled by the doe. Prompt treatment for does with retained placenta would be 1-3 cc oxytocin every 1 - 2 hours until she sheds it. If she has not shed it by 24 hours, she will need antibiotics too.

5. Examine does inside the uterus that show anxiety with straining after kidding. Examine for possibly another fetus.

6. Strip milk out of the udder, saving the colostrum to feed the kids and also check for mastitis, (stringy or dark colored milk). Water buckets should be removed when parturition is imminent to avoid drowning the kids. The kids are usually born within 1½ hours after the water

bag breaks. If the doe doesn't kid in half an hour, it may help to have the owner put her on a slope with her front end downhill for 1 hour, then release her to let her try again. If the kid is presented wrong, this allows it to fall back in and rearrange itself. Any manual assistance given should be very gentle because the uterus is relatively thin-walled and can rupture or tear. Attendant's hands should be washed with soap and clean water. Often a kid can be delivered with one leg still back.

It is of paramount importance that parturition (birth) takes place in a clean, draft-free and sheltered environment to reduce the chance of infection in the newborn. A rule of thumb: 14 square feet (approximately 1.2 meters by 1.2 meters), minimum for the pregnant doe and increased after birth. Weaned kids need a minimum of 4 to 5 square feet (approximately .37 meters x .37 meters) each.

About a week to 10 days before kidding, add a tablespoon of whole flax seed and 2 tablespoons of Red Wheat Bran to the doe's grain ration. It is a mild and lubricating laxative of the bowels, making kidding easier. Also, give wheat bran mash and warm drinking water to doe after kidding.

REPRODUCTIVE ORGANS OF BUCK

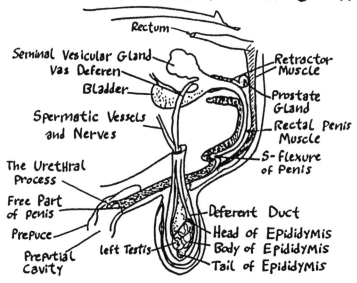

- Rectum
- Seminal Vesicular Gland
- Vas Deferen
- Bladder
- Spermatic Vessels and Nerves
- The UretHral Process
- Free Part of penis
- PrePuce
- Preputial Cavity
- left Testis
- Retractor Muscle
- Prostate Gland
- Rectal Penis Muscle
- S-flexure of Penis
- Deferent Duct
- Head of EpididyMis
- Body of EpididyMis
- Tail of EpididyMis

REPRODUCTIVE TRACT OF DOE

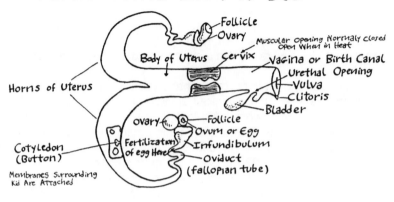

- Follicle
- Ovary
- Muscular Opening Normaly closed Open When in Heat
- Body of Uterus
- Cervix
- Vagina or Birth Canal
- Urethal Opening
- Vulva
- Clitoris
- Bladder
- Horns of Uterus
- Ovary
- Follicle
- Ovum or Egg
- Fertilization of egg Here
- Infundibulum
- Cotyledon (Button)
- Oviduct (fallopian tube)
- Membranes Surrounding Kid Are Attached

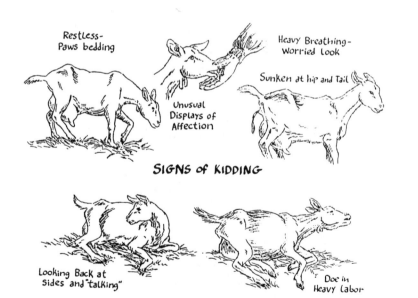

Restless-
Paws bedding

Heavy Breathing-
Worried Look

Sunken at hip and Tail

Unusual
Displays of
Affection

SIGNS of KIDDING

Looking Back at
Sides and "talking"

Doe in
Heavy Labor

The Birth Process

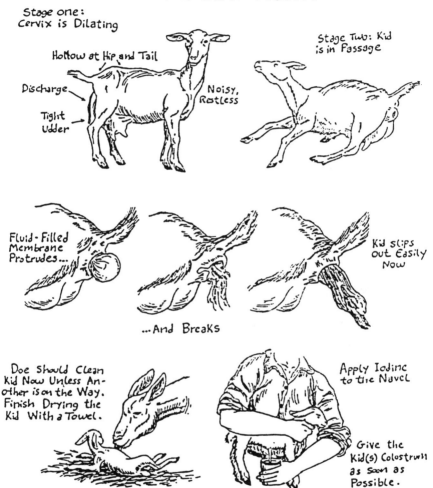

Stage one:
Cervix is Dilating

Stage Two: Kid is in Passage

Hollow at Hip and Tail

Discharge

Tight Udder

Noisy, Restless

Fluid-Filled Membrane Protrudes...

...And Breaks

Kid slips out Easily Now

Doe Should Clean Kid Now Unless Another is on the Way. Finish Drying the Kid With a Towel.

Apply Iodine to the Navel

Give the Kid(s) Colostrum as Soon as Possible.

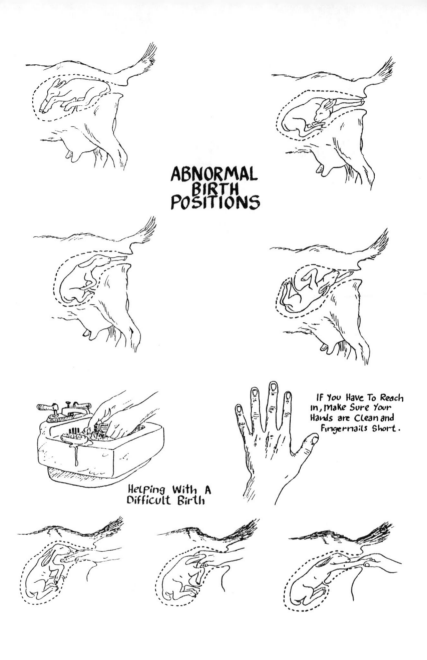

ABNORMAL BIRTH POSITIONS

IF You Have To Reach In, make Sure Your Hands are Clean and Fingernails Short.

Helping With A Difficult Birth

1."Health Care of the Goat and Sheep", R.A. Vanderhoof, VMD, 1987.

Section 14

The Udder and Milk Production

XIV. THE UDDER AND MILK PRODUCTION[1]

Many doctors prescribe goat's milk for humans for a number of maladies such as stomach ulcers and liver problems. But goat's milk is not a medicine. It is a very excellent food, and is more easily digested than cow's milk.

The great majority of goats are raised for milk and are managed much the same as dairy cows. They require milking twice daily and the usual length of lactation (milk production) is 305 days. This allows a 60 day dry period for the doe to replenish her body stores of nutrients before the next lactation.

When a doe kids or "freshens," it is a common practice to remove the kids and raise them separately from their dams. An average dairy goat will give about six to ten pounds (2.5 to 4.5 kg) of milk a day, and should be milked twice a day at approximately 12-hour intervals. A milking parlor or an area away from the main barn is needed for this purpose. The basic equipment needed to obtain milk for home use is a milking stand, clean bucket, sanitizing solution, teat dip, and milk strainer.

To avoid mastitis, does should be milked in an area free of dust and insects. Wash and dry each doe's udder thoroughly, using a separate disposable paper towel. Milk the first few squirts of milk into a strip cup or special container to check for abnormal milk.

Screen for mastitis milk. Any doe that has chronic mastitis is quite likely to infect other does and should be culled.

After the does have been milked, the milk should be run through a strainer to remove foreign material. Then it should be chilled to 50 degrees F (10 degrees C) or less within 30 minutes of milking and held at that temperature until use.

Composition of Milk

	Goat	Cow	Human
Fat %	3.8	3.67	3.6-4.7
Lactose %	4.54	4.80	7.18
Ash %	55	.65	.21
Protein %	3.21	3.50	1.19
Vit B$_1$ micrograms/100 ml	68	45	17
Calories/100 ml	70	69	68
Cholesterol mg/100 ml	17-39	7-10	

The supply of milk normally rises quite rapidly after kidding in response to the rapid growth demands of the young. The peak of production is commonly reached about two months after kidding. From the peak, the milk production curve gradually slopes downward. Age of the doe is a factor in milk production, the peak coming in the fourth or fifth year.

Milking procedures are similar to those for cows. Sanitation and general cleanliness are important. An elevated wooden stand aids cleanliness and spares the back of the milker. The best milk pails are seamless stainless steel and are hooded to keep out debris. A strip plate, strainer, and filter discs are also helpful. A goat can be milked by hand in 7-8 minutes.

DISEASES OF THE UDDER
Mastitis - Inflammation of the mammary glands from any cause. Mastitis produces changes in the milk secreting tissues.

Symptoms:
1. A straddling walk may be one of the first signs.
2. Milk can have clots or stringiness and reduced amount (and "off" color).
3. The udder is warm, swollen, hard, and usually painful and the milk is "off color.

Causes: Injuries to the udder or infection from a doe with mastitis.

Treatment:
1. Most mastitis cases are responsive to penicillin via intramammary infusions and intramuscular injections of the same for 5 to 7 days. First sterilize the end of teat well with a disinfectant, e.g., Betadine solution. Intrammary infusion medication - Generic — Techamerica Veterinary Products.

2. Frequent milking every 1 to 2 hours and massaging the effected half is very often sufficient treatment. Warm compresses or packs applied frequently are also helpful.

Prognosis: (Outcome): Guarded for recovery. Poor.

Good Udders

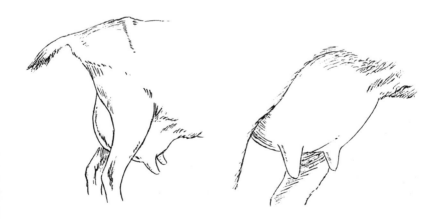

SUPERNUMERARY TEATS
A common problem is extra teats, double teats, and fish-tail teats with double orifices. Extra teats can be snipped off easily when very young.

PROPER MILKING MANAGEMENT
1. Sanitation. Prevent infections between animals.
   a) Use separate disposable paper towels or cloth towels for each animal - not a communal rag.
   b) Milker's hands should be washed between each milking.
2. Teat dipping. Recommended for goats.
   a) Organic iodine preparations, like Betadine, are best. Caution: iodine based preparations that have been accidentally frozen will cause severe irritation if used. Teats should be dipped following milking in an approved iodine solution, 5,000 to 10,000 ppm, (parts per million) which is a ½% to 1% solution. These iodine compounds should contain glycerol or lanolin. "Bovidine" or Betadine is one of the best aids in preventing the spread of mastitis.
3. Management.
   a) Every effort should be made to prevent healthy does from becoming infected by using good sanitation. Clean dry bedding areas are also important.
   b) Treatment for an animal that is already infected must be tried, but if not successful, the doe should be culled.

PASTEURIZATION
Pasteurizing equipment should be monitored carefully. Use a good, reliable thermometer.

Regular method: 145 degrees F (62 degrees C) for 30 minutes.

IMPORTANT DAIRY FACTS
1. Don't infuse the udder with irritating injectables, e.g., tetracycline hydrochloride which will cause udder to react violently.
2. The milking doe requires 3 times the amount of feed of a non-milking goat.
3. Be regular in both milking and feeding - this will teach the goat to be regular in her milk let-down.
4. Keep buck away from milking doe.
5. Only let the buck stay with the milking doe a short period of time as milk will absorb the male goat odor.
6. Heavy producers sometimes are milked three times a day, especially if the doe has leaking teats.
7. Doe at her best: production will be increased each year until about the fifth year.
8. The average life of a normal goat doe is considered to be 10 to 12 years.

UDDER IMPETIGO

Staphylococcus aureus infection is quite common. Erroneously called Goat Pox. People can become infected. Produces tiny ferruncles (pimples) with deep pussy abcesses in the skin. They are painful, extending deep into skin layers, and constitutes a very nasty situation in the dairy goat. Use Nolvasan Ointment until it clears up. Do not use water or a water preparation, which seems to cause them to spread. This disease is contagious and can spread to the whole herd.

Treatment: Dry pimple type: one time Copper Napthenate Ointment (Fort Dodge) followed by daily application of an ointment. The bovine udder infusion, e.g., "Dry Clox," cloxacillin benzathine (Fort Dodge) is effective.

CARE OF THE MILK EQUIPMENT

Mostly, pails and buckets are used. Only a few have milking machines. Most people fail to appreciate the importance of scrupulously clean equipment.

After cleaning equipment with detergent, follow with chlorine rinse around 200 parts/million, which would be 0.2 ml per liter (approximately one quart). Chlorine solution is inactivated by organic material, e.g., manure. So be sure there is no milk in buckets.

Iodine, 50 ppm or 0.05 ml per liter (quart), is satisfactory. Not as inactivated as much as chlorine in presence of organic material. Can use the color of the iodine solution as a measure of strength.

Detergent - use a good detergent in the quantity recommended and scrub vigorously. Always maintain the temperature of cleaning solutions. If below 105-110 degrees F (40-44 degrees C), can have a re-precipitation of fat in bucket.

Filter pads - to pour milk through. Cloth can be used or a manufactured special filter paper. This is important to remove any foreign material that dropped into milk while milking.

Cleanliness - clean the animals prior to milking. Wash udder with an iodine rinse. The milkers should wash their hands, both before and after milking.

HANDLING MILK

Cleanliness - cover milk in the bucket, prevent dirt and flies from contaminating.

Temperature - it is very important to cool the milk immediately to inhibit bacterial growth.

MILK OFF FLAVORS

Off flavors are a serious problem with goat milk.

1. Off flavor is present in the milk as it comes from the udder.

   a) Food flavors - volatile odors may be absorbed from the GI (stomach-intestinal) tract and pass via the blood system to the udder.

Onions, cabbage, turnips, and some weeds such as burdock are examples. If they are to be fed, feed small amounts immediately after milking, certainly no less than 4 hours before the next milking. The problem may occur in only one goat even though the whole herd is on the same diet. Odors from a dirty facility may be inhaled and reach the milk.

b) Conditions of health - off flavors may be secondary to systemic illnesses, including indigestion and metritis (inflammation of the uterus). Mastitis is a very important cause. A salty taste may develop, especially near the end of lactation. Occasionally a goat's milk will go off flavor each time she comes into heat.

2. Off flavor can develop while milk is standing. The udder should be washed and dried before each milking. This also stimulates milk "let down."

a) Bacterial action - the milk should be collected and stored in clean, sterilized utensils. Cool rapidly; pour the milk into pre-cooled containers and rush it to the refrigerator. Without refrigeration, milk should be consumed promptly.

b) Chemical action - Never mix raw and pasteurized or hot and cold raw milk.

c) Some goats always have poor-tasting milk, for which no correctable cause is found. This may be hereditary; the trait seems to run in certain families.

Proper Milking Procedures

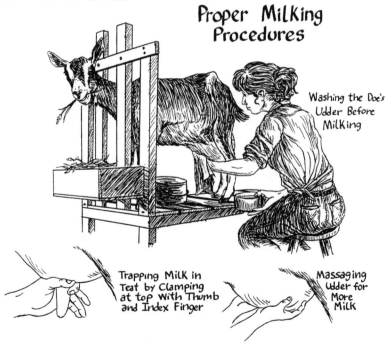

Washing the Doe's Udder Before Milking

Trapping Milk in Teat by Clamping at top with Thumb and Index Finger

Massaging Udder for More Milk

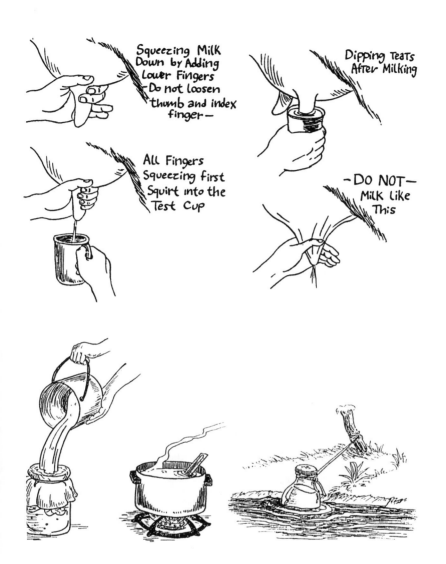

Squeezing Milk Down by Adding Lower Fingers —Do not loosen thumb and index finger—

Dipping Teats After Milking

All Fingers Squeezing first Squirt into the Test Cup

—DO NOT— Milk Like This

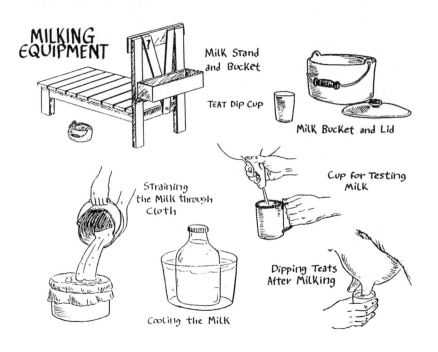

MILKING EQUIPMENT

Milk Stand and Bucket

TEAT DIP CUP

Milk Bucket and Lid

Straining the Milk through Cloth

Cup for Testing Milk

Cooling the Milk

Dipping Teats After Milking

Strip cup for testing
milk for lumps or stringiness.

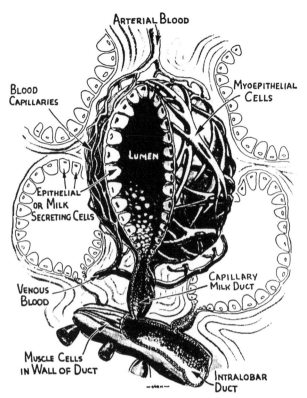

An alveous opened showing secretory cells, blood supplies, ducts and muscle cells. Drawing courtesy of Babson Bros. Co., Oakbrook, Illinois.

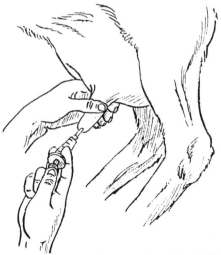

1. *"Health Care of the Goat and Sheep"*, R.A. Vanderhoof, VMD, 1987.

Section

Parasites

XV. PARASITES[12]

EXTERNAL PARASITES (live on outside of body)
EAR MITES - Psoroptic cuniculi, very common in ears of dairy goats. The mite lives deep in the ear canals.
   Symptoms: Head shaking, ear scratching, scabs in ears, and trying to put a foot in ear. Carry head to one side or tip head or walk in circles. La Manchas can have severe infestations. May be a discharge from the ear and may see whitish scaly exudate in ear.
   Treatment: cattle screw-worm (eartick medicine) sprays containing lindane. Preparations used on dogs and cats for ear mites, e.g., Rotenone=1 part to 3 parts mineral oil, and work down into ear. Mitox-Carbaryl N-Methylcarbamazine (Sevin). Goats don't like to have ear manipulated. Best to treat again in 2 weeks. Ivermectin or dectomax injectable (1cc/110 lbs.) or pour-on (1cc/36 lbs.) are also effective.

   FLEAS - are sometimes a problem in kids, but condition is rare. Usually acquire from barn cats. Treatment: Sevin, Lindane spray, and other flea preparations such as pyrethins used for dogs and cats.

FLY STRIKE - Massive egg deposits, rapidly hatch into maggots.
   Treatment: Fly repellents, e.g., pine tar. Diesel starting fluid will work immediately to kill maggots. The main ingredient is ether. Also straight ether or chloroform.
   Maggots are very devastating to goats. As few as 2 or 3 under the skin can sometimes cause death.

BITING LICE - Bovicola caprae or Damalinia are less common and are large enough to see with a magnifying glass, especially on the back and neck. They are yellow orange to brown in color and have broad head. They live on scales of dandruff and skin. They burrow into hair follicles. Usually cause severe pruritis (itching). Will see more in the winter and spring months.
   Treatment: None are approved for lactating animals. Coumaphos, (Co- Ral) .03% dust, or "pour on" (pour on small amount on back of animal). This is good and especially safe for kids. Clip hair - renders insecticide more efficient. Dust with Co-Ral powder or apply a solution 1 lb. of 25% Co-Ral powder in 100 gallons of water - spray on. Repeat treatment in 10 to 14 days. Ivermectin is effective for sucking lice but not biting lice.
   In treating external parasites, Malathion or Sevin are used. Particularly good for biting lice in Angora goats. Can also mix Co-Ral in with this. Pyretherins are also effective for external parasites.

   SUCKING LICE - Linognathus stenopsis, larger than biting louse. Lice live on the animal. They have no intermediate host. Lice are introduced to the herd by new animals or from a show. Inspect "new" goats closely for lice when introducing to your premises. Mostly found in winter and spring. Prevalent on sides of neck and underline around udder. Can see nits (small, developing or baby lice) in the hair (brown). They spend their entire life cycle on the goat. They are visible to the naked eye; they have a narrow head and are bluish in color. They pierce the skin to feed and are heavy blood suckers. They can cause severe anemia, even fatal, especially in kids. A heavy infestation can kill a young goat. They may have central nervous system (incoordination) signs and are very weak from anemia (blood loss) and cannot tolerate stress. Tend to multiply more rapidly on young, sick, or debilitated animals. They may hibernate (become inactive) in skin folds and crevice during hot summer months, then have a sudden appearance in cool weather.

Treatment: Ivermectin or Co-Ral Spray or dipping and repeat in 10 to 14 days as this is their life cycle span. Premises don't need treatment. The dosage for Ivermectin is 1 ml per 110 lbs. (50 kg) body weight S.C. It can be injected S.C. or given orally.

MANGE[3] - A contagious skin disease caused by very small mites not visible to the naked eye. They belong to the spider family, (they have eight legs.) They burrow into the layers of the skin and spend their life-cycle there. Two types are considered below that effect goats.

Psoroptic mange - Cause: Psoroptic cuniculi

Symptoms: usually infests the ears but sometimes spreads to the head, neck and body, causing severe irritation. This occurs particularly in Angora goats in which the mohair is considerably damaged.

Treatment: The course is chronic (long lasting) but the prognosis (outcome) is good. Lactating (milking) dairy goats should be treated only with lime-sulfur solution, while all other goats can be treated with dips or sprays containing coumaphos (0.3) = (Co-Ral) Injectible ivermectin has proven effective against most mange mite species. Inject 1 cc per 110 lbs. under the skin. Repeat weekly until the disease is seen to be in remission.

Demodectic mange - Cause: Demodex caprae
These mites invade hair follicles (the root of hair shaft) and sebaccous (oil) glands causing loss of hair and abcesses. Normally the disease is limited to many small nodules, especially on the brisket (under neck), lower neck, forearm and shoulder, but the problem may generalize (become widespread). The nodules ranging in size pinhead to hazelnut, contain a thick, waxy, grayish material that can be easily expressed. Numerous demodectic mites are found in this material. In some countries, this infection can cause great damage to the hides.

Treatment: Injectable ivermectin has proven effective against most mange mite species. Inject 1 cc per 110 lbs. under the skin. Repeat weekly until the disease is seen to be in remission.

NOSE BOTS - Oestrus ovis, a large grub (larva)
Commom in goats housed with sheep.
   Symptoms:
   1. Chronic discharge from nose (both sheep and goats).
   2. Snuffling (both sheep and goats).
   3. Goats may try to hide indoors during hot fly season.
   4. Larvae live within the sinuses of the head.
Treatment: Ivermectin, 1 ml per 110 lbs. (50 kg) body weight S.C.

RINGWORM
   A fungus. There are several species and all are contagious. Body distribution - head, ears, neck, generally. Mostly are scaly circular lesions - grey short-hair areas - hair shafts broken off short. Highly contagious to other animals and humans.
   Treatment:
   1. Captan—(available as ortho rose dust) — dosage 1 oz. of powder (2 tablespoonful per qt. of water) wiped on lesions or sprayed on animals for 5 days.
   2. Iodine—(Betadine) wiped on or sprayed on for 5 days. Repeat as needed.
   3. 5%sodium hypochlorite - (1:10 chlorine bleach - apply to lesions as needed)
   4. 10% thiabendazole (TBZ) in glycerine. Apply topically daily for two weeks.

A Dipping Vat

INTERNAL PARASITES

A major problem in goats and an important cause of anemia (blood loss or a deficiency of red corpuscles in the blood). Most can be diagnosed by gross examination of the feces, or by employing special techniques known as fecal flotation or fecal sedimentation tests where the parasite eggs are examined under a microscope.

Moderate Symptoms:
1. Rough hair coat and dandruff
2. Anemia (lack of normal pink color of the white of the eye and inside of lips and the gums)
3. Diarrhea
4. Poor appetite
5. Reduced milk production
6. Poor growth
7. Increased susceptibility to disease

Major symptoms in advanced cases:
1. Bottle jaw - see illustration
2. Rapid heart beat
3. Labored breathing
4. Weakness
5. Death

Goats tend to have more internal parasites than dairy cows, especially in confined management. When treating goats for parasites, it is very important to treat all animals on the premises at the same time.

"Bottle Jaw"

LUNG WORMS

Live in the air passages of the lungs. They can be from 3/4 to 2 1/2 inches, (18 mm to 6.5 cm) long. Their presence increases the animal's susceptibility to pneumonia with coughing.

Treatment:
Ripercol or Levamisol - 2 ml per 100 lbs. (45.4 kg) body weight SQ.
Ivermectin - 1 ml per 110 lbs. (50 kg) body weight SQ.
Mebendazole - 10 mg. per kg. orally.
Albendazole - 10 mg. per kg. orally.

STOMACH AND INTESTINAL WORMS

Also called hair worms, they live in the stomach and intestines and are blood suckers. Kids are highly susceptible and most adults are more resistant, but may remain carriers and shedders of the worm eggs. See diagram of life cycle on page 110.

Symptoms:
Blackish green diarrhea, depression, abdominal pain, weight loss, rough, dry hair coat, bottle jaw, dehydration, and death.

Treatment:
Ivermectin or Dectomax injectable - 1 cc per 110 lbs. (50 kg)
Albendazole - 10 mg. per kg. orally. It should not be given in the first 50 days of pregnancy.
Mendendazole - 10 mg. per kg. orally.
Oxfendazole - 10 mg. per kg. orally.

TAPEWORMS

Not life-threatening like other parasites. Not a big problem but maybe underestimated. One type spends part of its life cycle in bedding and in soil. Flat, white, segmented ribbons live in the small intestine and are passed in the feces.

Symptoms:
1. Segments of tape worm may be found hanging on the hair in perineal area (under tail) or in the feces.
2. A slight diarrhea.

Treatment: Mebendazole (Telmin) and Fenbendazole (panacur). Albendazole is most effective. Ivermectin is not effective. See diagram of life cycle on page 109.

LIVER FLUKE (Flat Worms)

Must have a snail in pasture (usually a body of water - (lake) that carries the metacercariae (young developing fluke) - waits on encystment inside a capsule on the vegetation and is consumed by host. See diagram of life cycle on page 110.

1. Emaciation, anemia, lethargy, weight loss. It is estimated that an adult fluke ingests .3 to .5 ml of blood per day, so 150 flukes could be taking 45 to 95 ml of blood from the animal per day.
2. Cause of inflammation and tissue death as they migrate through the liver.
3. Distended painful abdomen.
4. May cause disease in goats that share their pasture with deer.
5. Decreased milk production.
6. Bottle jaw (swelling under the jaw).

Prevention:
1. Good nutrition.
2. Snail control - drain or fence off marshes.
3. Treat marshes or ponds to kill snails.

Treatment/Control:
Control:
1. Fecal sedimentation test: A microscopic examination for worm eggs in the feces should be checked several times a year.
2. All new goats, or goats returning from fairs or breeding on different premises, should be quarantined until determined to be free of internal parasites.
3. Manure control - use adequate feeders, waterers, where animals can't defecate manure onto the feed.
4. Pasture management:
   a) Do not overstock the field, paddock, or pasture.
   b) Mow the grass frequently if possible so the grass is exposed to direct sunlight - this stops development of many parasites.
   c) Keep deer out of pastures if feasible.
   d) Include both goats and sheep in the same deworming program.
   e) "Safe pasture." Alternate or rotate pastures with cattle and horses as they don't have the same species of parasites in their systems.

Treatment: Flukes are not susceptible to most wormers. Albendazole is the drug of choice if available. Deer and snail population should be kept separate from goats.

1. De-worm goats in late fall and move to safe pasture. Repeat again in late spring or 2 weeks before kidding.
   2. "Periparturient rise" in parasites - parasites will reproduce rapidly around kidding time and infect the kids. So treat all does 2 weeks before kidding. Repeat every 3 weeks for 3 more treatments.
   3. Moving goats to a safe pasture after worming is very helpful in maintaining a reduced parasite load.
   Other Flukicides include:
   1) Clorsulan
   2) Triclabendazole*
   3) Rafoxanide*
   4) Closantel*
   5) Oxyxlozanide*
   6) Nitroxynil*
   *All these are listed in the Oxfam/FARM - Africa Publication, *IMPROVING GOAT PRODUCTION IN THE TROPICS, A Manual for Development Workers,* by Christie Peacock.

COCCIDIOSIS

An intestinal disease of primarily young animals caused by a protozoa. One of the most frustrating parasitic infections encountered by the goat owner. Coccidia can be considered one of the leading killers of young goats under 4 months of age. The life cycle is complex. Kids born in the spring are the most vulnerable and clinical signs appear 4 to 8 weeks after exposure.

Symptoms:
1. A high percentage of kids are affected.
2. Weakness.
3. Not eating - loss of appetite.
4. Losing weight, chronically poor gains.
5. A watery diarrhea with blood and straining, but usually rare. It will sometimes be a gray-green color
6. Dehydration.
7. Rough hair coat.
8. Anemia.
9. Sudden death - can be high if not treated, but usually around 10%.

Coccidia infection may be acquired from contaminated water and feed or pasture or by licking contaminated wool or hair of an infected animal. The well fed animal is just as susceptible to coccidia as the malnourished one.

If a kid is weak and unthrifty, consider coccidiosis. The severity of symptoms depends upon how many occysts are ingested. The majority recover but will have a setback in growth and decreased performance. Even though immunity develops, the animal may continue to shed occysts for the rest of its life.

Prevention:
1. Pasture rotation.
2. Raise kids on elevated, slatted floors or pens.
3. Avoid small grassy areas for exercise.
4. Clean environment - dry, clean lots. Keep clean of manure or dirty bedding and compost this if possible.
5. Isolate sick and newly acquired individuals.
6. Separate kids from adults.
7. To aid in the prevention of coccidiosis in artificially reared dairy goats, the kids should be put in small, age-matched groups in outside portable or elevated pens that are moved to clean ground periodically.
8. Arrange and establish feeders so that neither kids nor adults can contaminate feed with their manure. Prevent the kids from jumping into the feed troughs.
9. Stressful situations: (must be kept to a minimum)
   a) Avoid overcrowding
   b) Avoid changes in surroundings
   c) Avoid sudden changes in feed
   d) Avoid travel as much as possible
   e) Lessen hot weather effects by using shades, barns, etc.
   f) Weaning can be a stressful situation
   g) Stress allows the propagation of the coccidia to gain a foothold in the animal.

If a herd problem with coccidia exists, start the kids on a coccidiostat, (a medicine that inhibits coccidia growth) one to two weeks before introducing them to older animals. Maintain them on the coccidiostat for 6 weeks.

Treatment: "Corid" 9.6% solution in drinking water at 16 oz. per 100 gallons, (473.2 ml per 378.L) for 5 days. Then use solution of 8 oz. per 100 gallons (236.8 ml per 378. liters) for 21 days. Re-worm daily for 5 to 7 days. "Bovatec" can be incorporated in a pre-creep feed.

Prevention: Amprolium, Lasalocid, Sulfamethazine, Deccoquanate, Nitrofurazone, or Rumensin. Amprolium - "Corid" 9.6% solution in drinking water at 18 oz. per 100 gallons (236.8 ml per 378 liters) for 21 days. Bovatec can be incorporated in a pre-creep feed.

SUMMARY OF INTERNAL PARASITISM

This is one of the most important problems of all animals. Goats are the most susceptible of all livestock species to parasitism. Contaminated feed and water are the major problems. To produce goat milk from healthy animals with a low level of parasitism, it is best to keep them in the dry lot - feed them green forage through the fence with a key hole feeder - and avoid fecal (manure) contamination in the feeder and water. That's the best way to control internal parasites in goats.

PARASITE CONTROL IN GENERAL

Do's:
1. Do maintain clean, dry, warm housing.
2. Do keep available supply of fresh water.
3. Do rotate pastures.
4. Do keep kids separate from adults.
5. Do feed well balanced diet in adequate amounts.
6. Do discuss problems with your animal health advisor.
7. Do observe goats daily.

Don'ts:
1. Don't mix other livestock with goats.
2. Don't have feeders where animals can climb into them.
3. Don't allow water supply to become contaminated with droppings or bedding.
4. Don't graze in swampy areas.
5. Don't mix newly purchased goats with herd until proper isolation (about 4 weeks) is observed and vaccinations are done. (Quarantine)
6. Avoid any or all stressful situations.

TICKS

Ticks are a serious problem and a good program of management must be used to prevent fatal diseases, such as Anaplasmosis and Heart-water disease. Treatment is best accomplished by the use of sprays or dipping, using Co-Ral, Neguson, Diaxinon, etc.

LIFE CYCLE OF TICK

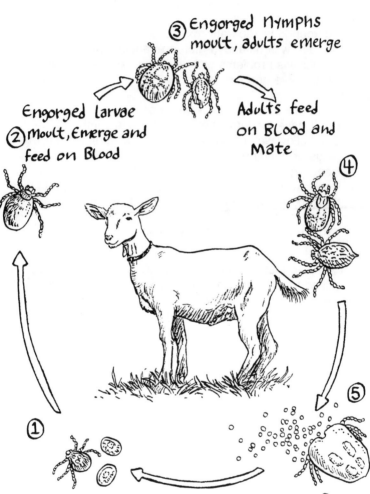

③ Engorged nymphs moult, adults emerge

Engorged larvae
② moult, Emerge and feed on Blood

Adults feed on Blood and Mate

④

⑤

①

Eggs Hatch, larvae Emerge, Climb on Host and feed on Blood

Engorged female falls to Ground and Lays Eggs

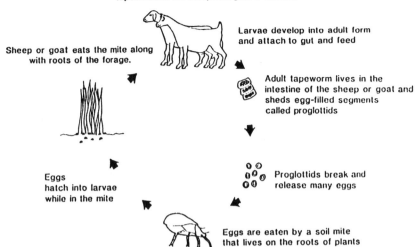

Mite digested away from the larval tapeworm in the sheep and goat's stomach

Sheep or goat eats the mite along with roots of the forage.

Larvae develop into adult form and attach to gut and feed

Adult tapeworm lives in the intestine of the sheep or goat and sheds egg-filled segments called proglottids

Eggs hatch into larvae while in the mite

Proglottids break and release many eggs

Eggs are eaten by a soil mite that lives on the roots of plants

Typical Life Cycle of the Tapeworm

Life Cycle of Coccidia

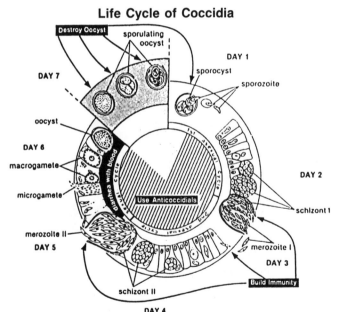

Life cycle of ovian coccidia (E. tenella) similar to the ones found in goats; showing where anticoccidial drugs are effective. Drawing courtesy of Feedstuffs Publishers, Minneapolis, Minnesota, November 1, 1982.

Life Cycle of a Typical Stomach Worm

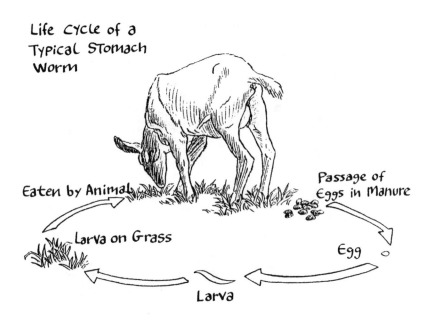

Eaten by Animal

Passage of Eggs in Manure

Larva on Grass

Egg

Larva

LIVER FLUKE - Life Cycle

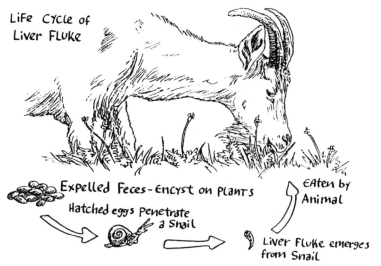

Life Cycle of Liver Fluke

Expelled Feces - Encyst on Plants

Hatched eggs penetrate a Snail

Eaten by Animal

Liver Fluke emerges from Snail

1. Material derived from *"Health Care of the Goat and Sheep"*, R.A. Vanderhoof, VMD, 1987.
2. Extension Goat Handbook, Section A-2, page 2.
3. The Veterinary Merck Manual, 7th Edition, page 816.

Section 16

Diseases of the Kid

XVI. DISEASES OF THE KID[1]

FEEDING KIDS

Most dairy goat kids are taken from their dams at birth and bottle fed. The first meal for a newborn kid should be colostrum. This is the first milk that a doe produces, and it contains antibodies to protect the young kid from infection until its own immune system can take over. Quite often, goat raisers simply let the kids nurse their dams for their first meal. The milk that a doe produces for three days after freshening is not acceptable for human use.

Kid goats may be raised on goat milk (first choice), cow milk (second choice), or commercial milk replacer (third choice). A kid should be started on 5-6 oz., 148 to 177 ml three times a day. Within three weeks they should be able to consume a pint, 473 ml, three times a day.

Cow's milk or commercial replacer

Kids can be weaned as early as six weeks of age if they are eating other feed well. They will start to nibble at hay leaves by about one week of age if hay is available to them. They should be offered a very palatable concentrate ration if available after about three weeks of age. Sometimes does are allowed to raise their own kids. In this situation, the does should be checked daily to make sure their udders are being emptied of milk. If not, the doe's udder may become lopsided or she may be in danger of contracting mastitis. Some producers lock the kids up at night, milk the does in the morning, then turn the kids back in with their dams during the day to reduce bottle feeding and milking.

If the kid fails to suck and get milk, it must be helped. It may be necessary to open its mouth and milk the teat into it.

If you want to milk the mother doe for home use, do not allow the kid to stay with the doe during the night time. Put the kid in a separate pen and allow it to be with the doe only during the day.

DISBUDDING NEONATAL (Newborn) KIDS

Horns can be a source of injury to other animals or to humans, especially if they are on the buck, however in some areas the horns should be left intact to allow protection against predators. Some goats are hornless. Examine for horn buds, which can be detected at birth.

1. Do as early as 2 days old, as horn grow extremely fast.
2. Inoculate with tetanus antitoxin, half of a vial that contains 1500 units.
3. Best to use an electric disbudding iron made for goats and when heated, the end must reach a cherry-red color, a 3/4 inch (18mm) diameter steel pipe with wood handle can be heated on one end and used very satisfactorily. Apply heated disbudder iron over horn button for about 5 seconds, and not more than 7 seconds, let head cool for 15 to 20 seconds and remove the horn cap and re-burn over the bloody stump to prevent the growth of scurs. Don't be too aggressive. Be sure the burned area is at least ¼ to ½ inches from the base of the horn bud - if not, scurs (degenerate, misshapen horns) will grow. Caution: if head is over-heated there can be brain damage. Can destroy the musk patches or scent glands at the same time. Scent glands are slightly posterior (toward rear and medial (toward the middle) from horn buttons. If hot iron is applied for too long a period of time, there is danger of producing a "post dehorning encephalitis" caused by burning the surface of the brain.

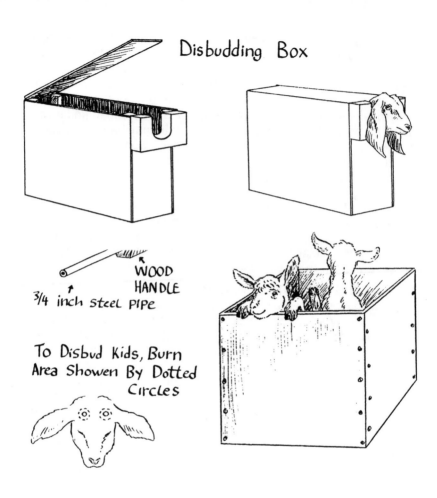

Disbudding Box

WOOD HANDLE

3/4 inch steel PIPE

To Disbud Kids, Burn Area Showen By Dotted Circles

PNEUMONIA PREVENTION

Can grab newly born kid by hind legs and swing it around in order to throw fluids out of lungs. Use an infant rubber syringe or ear syringe to extract fluid from nose. If weak or not breathing, can use artificial respiration. Close one nostril and blow into other one to inflate lungs.

If extremely cold, the kids may be suffering from hypothermia (subnormal body temperature). Put this baby kid in a bathtub of warm water, 104 degrees F (40 degrees C). This is the fastest method of raising their body temperature to normal. Heat lamps are also used but be careful of burning the kid. They can be rolled in a blanket; held close to a person's body and rubbed or put next to heated rocks.

Contracted (tightened) tendons causing "knuckling over" are quite common, but usually will be self correcting in several days.

WEAK AND STARVING KIDS
1. Usually need heat and food.
2. In their very weak condition they will often eat dirt and hair.
3. Be sure they are getting milk when nursing - does rarely could have plugged teats. Kid's tail will wag if getting milk.
4. Or give oral electrolytes. Several commercial preparations are available, like Pedialyte or Gatorade, or try the following home-made formula, which can be given by mouth or stomach tube, small amounts, frequently.

2 teaspoons of common table salt. (10 grams).

1 teaspoon of baking soda (sodium bicarbonate) 5 grams.

8 tablespoons of crystalline dextrose, honey, or white corn syrup (not cane syrup), (120 grams).

Mix in 1 gallon of warm water. (4 liters). A 10 lb. (4.5 kg), kid should receive 6 to 8 oz. (177 to 236 ml) by nursing bottle or drench, three or four times per day[2].

MANAGEMENT OF NEWBORN KIDS
Feeding young stock. The kid should be fed as much as it wants in 6 feeds per day. Nipple feeding is more natural but pan feeding from the beginning simplifies feeding and sterilizing procedures. The milk must be at body temperature. By two weeks of age, the kid will be drinking up to 2 quarts, 1.9 liters, of milk a day; this is the maximum amount to be fed kid of any age. At two weeks old, add good roughage and a mineral lick or clean dirt to supply iron and copper. Normal growth rate is 0.5 lbs., 226 gm, gain per day. The kid can be weaned as early as 5 weeks of age or 20 pounds, 9 kg. Extra goat milk may be frozen for as long as a year or fed back to the doe. Colostrum may be frozen in ice cube trays, (one cube per kid), to provide for emergencies when the mother's colostrum may not be available. Cow colostrum is better than nothing. Cow's milk may be substituted freely for goat's milk in raising kids. Scours (diarrhea) in the young kid may be caused by dirty utensils, cold milk, or overfeeding. Kids that become cold and weak need special care. Keep them warm and give high energy food, such as honey and sugar and electrolytes, (see above).

When kid diets are changed, it should be done gradually. They should be bottle fed so that the suckling reflex is maintained. Goat's milk is the best diet, especially in the first 4 weeks. Can use cow's milk after the first 4 weeks.

A common feeding practice which prevents kids from learning to eat much grain and forage is too frequent feeding of milk and feeding too much milk. Twice-daily feeding is adequate for kids after they are three days old and a practical maximum of two pounds, 907 gram, of milk daily should be set for animals to be reared as herd replacements. As kids approach weaning age, gradually adding warm water to the milk they are fed, will provide them with necessary fluids for rumen development and ease the stress of weaning them. Grain and hay fed to young kids should be selected for them mainly on the basis of palatability. Hay which may appear to the feeder to be the best quality, may not be as palatable or acceptable as other hay.

Kids can be weaned after 8 weeks. 12 to 16 weeks is more natural and they do better. Gradual weaning is often most practical.

Cold or chilling stress can be a significant cause of early mortality in newborn kids and presumably a risk factor for the subsequent development of pneumonia. Cold wind can be particularly devastating.

Animals at high risk of becoming weak (stressed), include multiple births, premature, or limp and weak kids, and those born to dams in poor condition. Those animals with moderate hypothermia (35 to 39 degrees C, approximately 96 to 100 degrees F) should be dried, given an additional ration of colostrum, or fed milk substitute and removed to shelter. Hypothermia (under 37 degrees C, 98.6 degrees F) is best treated by artificial warming. A water bath of 104 degrees F, (40 degrees C), is probably the fastest method to restore body temperatures to normal. Coats can be made from T-shirts, sweaters, or jackets or even plastic garbage bags with appropriate holes cut, to help conserve body heat.

Kid wearing a T-shirt or jacket

KID SCOURS (Diarrhea)

A very effective precaution against diarrhea in kids - regularity in feeding milk that has been heated to body temperature. Or, if colostrum is available, the use of which will control stubborn scours. Bovine colostrum can be used at the rate of approximately 5% of body weight of the kid. First, take off, or remove food entirely or reduce drastically for a day.

Antibiotics:
Neomycin - use orally for a general rule of thumb for scours.
Other useful drugs:
Gentocin (a wide spectrum antiobiotic)
Vetisulid (a sulfa).
Albon (a sulfa) Sulfadimethoxine
Val Syrup (Fort Dodge) an excellent product for pediatric use.
Probiotic - a lactobacillus preparation This is excellent in restoring normal level of microorganisms in the digestive tract.
Kaobiotic (Upjohn) Kaolin-pectin with neomycin.
This is an excellent preparation, usually very effective and safe.
When the feces firms up, then the animal can go back on feed, but gradually! Try not to have on full feed until 3 to 5 days.
Dehydration of the body is of prime concern. Use pinch test*, (the degree and length of time the skin stays pinched is the degree of dehydration), for rough determination. Use oral rehydration fluids.
*See illustration on page 24

NURSING AND FEEDING KIDS

When the tail is wiggling, it means he's getting milk.
Kids should have access to hay, and a grain-based creep feed, (a pen or enclosure specially constructed so that the kid can enter through a small opening, but not the adult animals), as early as 1 week of age. They can be weaned when they are readily eating a large handful of grain per day; this should occur approximately 5 weeks of age, and no later than 8 weeks of age.

MANAGEMENT PROCEDURES

Navels of kids should be treated immediately following birth with iodine solution Betadine iodine. Check them for birth defects. Disbud kids at 3 days to 2 weeks of age, preferably with a hot iron made for that purpose. Castrate buck kids and remove accessory supernumerary teats from doe kids, and give tetanus antitoxin vaccine.
Selenium/vitamin E shots, (BoSe), should be given in areas where the deficiency occurs. Give immunizations for enterotoxemia and tetanus at 4 and 6 weeks of age. Anticoccidial drugs may be necessary in some herds. Start a record with health, reproduction, production and disposition information on each kid.
To administer fluids, use the oral route or give SQ.

To determine between stillbirth and living birth: if the dead kid or lamb was living when born and walked on its feet, the thin seal covering the sole of the hoof will be broken or disturbed, while if the animal was born dead or aborted, this seal should be intact.

WETHERS (CASTRATED MALES)

Wethers fed on substantial amounts of grain are prone to develop urinary calculi. Reducing grain consumption, adding ammonium chloride (7-10 g/head/day for a 30 kg kid) to the diet, keeping the Ca:P ratio around 2:1, and keeping the magnesium level low will help.

CONTROLLING COCCIDIOSIS IN KIDS

Kids with coccidiosis, usually over 4 weeks of age show slight diarrhea, diagnosis can be made by fecal microscopic examination.

For treatment use sulfa (sulfamethazine) on kids while on milk. When 2 to 3 weeks of age, put sulfa in their milk once daily for 7 days, then stop and repeat in 2 weeks. Can repeat this treatment. Another critical period is when kids are not on such a preventative program and stressed at weaning.

Amprolium (Corid) is effective very early in the life cycle of this disease. If used, should be given to kids early in life - on for 3 weeks and off for 2 weeks.

Deccox - used as a continuous treatment by adding to feed. Available in bulk form in a soybean meal base so it can be mixed at home. Deccox has a wide margin of safety. Start kids on it in their grain mix. The kids have to consume the grain to get this medication.

1. Material derived from *"Health Care of the Goat and Sheep"*, R.A. Vanderhoof, VMD, 1987.
2. Extension Goat Handbook, page G4-4. Diarrheal Diseases, J.L. Ayers, Los Olivas, CA.
3. Merck Manual

Section 17

Foot Diseases

A malformed hoof

XVII. FOOT DISEASE[1]

LAMENESS

Lameness among goats is one of the most common problems faced by producers, and can lead to other complications if not treated and controlled.

PROBLEMS OF HOOVES

These involve horny areas of the foot and its associated structures.

Causes - bruising from rough ground or stones, punctures from sharp objects, laminitis (inflammation beneath the hoof wall) usually caused by stress or dietary changes, wet conditions, separations of the white line (the white-colored area that joins the wall of the hoof to the sole) poor hoof trimming practices, foot rot causing bacteria (Fusobacterium necrophorous and Bacteriodes nodosus), and various viruses including foot-and-mouth virus.

When hooves are not properly trimmed, the feet become distorted and misshapen and the foot develops pockets and crevices. If foot rot bacteria get into the hoof, these pockets can harbor the infection for long periods.

Infectious causes like bacteria and certain viruses are introduced into the flock by addition of new animals, and then spread by both indirect and direct contact.

Treatment: Examine the feet and depending on the cause, trimming, footbaths in disinfectants, antibiotics, and even vaccination may be indicated.

For Prevention, avoid exposure of animals to sharp objects and wet conditions, and regularly trim hooves. If infectious causes have been diagnosed in your area, avoid additions of new animals when possible.

TRIMMING OVERGROWN HOOVES

Tools for trimming:
1. Pocket knife or a jack knife with medium size blade. Must be sharp.
2. A hoof knife - the same type used on horses.
3. Foot rot shears.
4. Hoof nippers.
5. File or rasp.

Frequency: The normal goat on soft bedding needs frequent trimming. Monthly examination and attention is best.

Instruction: Properly trimmed hoofs are a must. Untrimmed or poorly trimmed hoofs can cause serious lameness. The more often you trim them, the less often you have to cut them off. Trim the wall so that it is parallel to the coronary band and does not roll over the sole. The soft heel may need to be shortened to prevent the spreading of the toes. Always cut from heel to toe.[2]

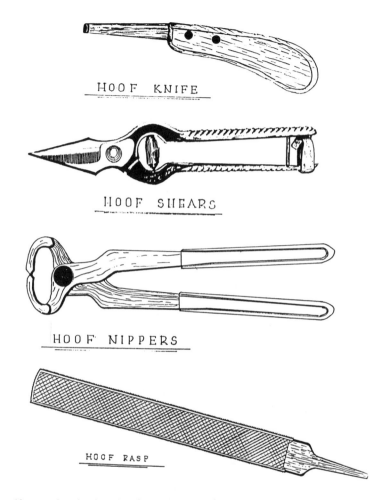

HOOF KNIFE

HOOF SHEARS

HOOF NIPPERS

HOOF RASP

If you trim the hoofs often, you won't need to trim much of the pad, if any. Sometimes you may have to trim some of the heel in order to get the bottom level. If some of the pad has to be trimmed, do it in thin slices. Stop when the pad turns pinkish color, as you may draw blood if you go too deep. Work on one toe at a time. With the first cut, remove the outer wall. Then level the heel and pad to make the hoof floor level. It is seldom necessary to remove much of the pad. If it is, take care not to cut too deep as this will draw blood.

When you finish the first toe, begin on the other. Take care to trim both toes so that when the foot is placed on the ground, one toe is not longer than the other.

Note that the well trimmed hoof does not have an overlapping wall. The hoof wall is level and clean.[3]

DIG DIRT OUT FROM TOES →

PARE HEELS TO SAME LEVEL AS TOES.

TRIM AWAY ALL LOOSE EXCESS NAIL. TRIM PARALLEL TO HOOF HAIRLINE.

SNIP AWAY THE LITTLE FLAP THAT GROWS BETWEEN TOES →

FINISH THE TRIM BY PARING THE SOFT HEEL TISSUE TILL HOOF SURFACE IS SMOOTH AND FLAT.

FINISHED.
Coronay band

The procedure for trimming the rear feet is the same as for the front feet.

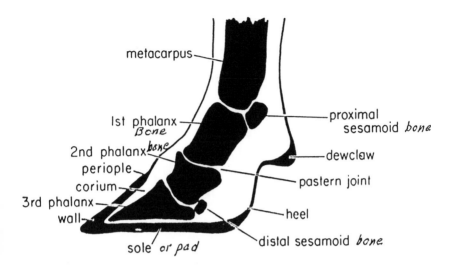

Cross section of goat foot. Drawing courtesy of G.F. W. Haenlein, University of Delaware.

1. Material derived from "Health Care of the Goat and Sheep", R. A. Vander-hoof, VMD, 1998
2. Ibid, page 10
3. Ibid, page 11
4. "Your Dairy Goat", A Western Regional Extension Publication, revised by July 1981, WREP #47, pages 10 and 11.

Section 18

Slaughtering Goats for Meat

*Raising Goats for "Milk and Meat", a Heifer International Training Course, third printing, July 1985, Rosalee Sinn.

XVIII. SLAUGHTERING GOATS FOR MEAT[1]

Goats are thin animals by nature and meat from young goats is as tender as lamb but normally has less fat covering. The meat is particularly sought after for barbecues and for holidays of some ethnic groups.[2]

SELECTING ANIMALS
A listing of those animals which could be slaughtered.
 1. Not suitable for breeding, i.e., animals with genetic defects. Note: If abnormal conditions are evident, further inspection by a qualified person, such as a veterinarian, would be advisable. Diseased animals should not be slaughtered for human food.
 2. Surplus breeding stock
 3. Unthrifty animals
 4. Poor producers
 5. Older animals
 6. Male kids that have been castrated.[3]

HANDLING OF ANIMALS PRIOR TO SLAUGHTER
 1. Withhold feed of all kinds - both hay and grain - for 24 hours prior to slaughter.
 2. Do provide plenty of water.
 3. Place animals in a clean, well-bedded area.
 4. Do not excite animals prior to slaughter. Do not pinch hide or beat with a stick because you will bruise the meat and it will spoil more quickly. Slaughter in the cool of the day. If refrigeration is not available, plan to slaughter only animals that can be eaten in 24 hours. Otherwise, you may want to preserve meat by salting, drying, etc.

PREPARATION FOR SLAUGHTER
Plan to slaughter in an area with a concrete floor or put legs on your slaughtering cradle to keep the animal's carcass clean.

Make a Hanging Stick   **Make a Slaughtering Cradle**

Have plenty of clean, cold water available.

EQUIPMENT

1. Hammer or pistol (for stunning, if preferred).
2. Sharp knife and sharpening stone, or sharpening steel for putting edge on the knife.
3. Rack to hang hide on, meat saw (if available).
4. Container for blood.

SLAUGHTERING

1. Halter animal. Hold about 6 inches, (15 cm) distance.

2. Draw an imaginary cross between ears and eyes. Where the cross intersects is the place to strike the stunning blow. Use small blunt instrument like a hammer, or shoot with a pistol. Animal will probably not die, only be stunned.

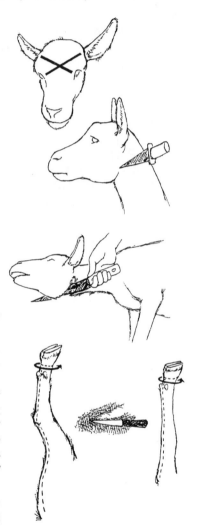

3. Put the stick knife below the ear and at the base of the jaw stick through to other side. Cutting edge should be pointed out. Speed is important. Let the blood flow freely. When you are sure animal is through bleeding, pull chin back until you can see neck bones. Sever windpipe, sever head.

4. Let animal bleed a couple of minutes until it has quit thrashing.

5. Put animal into cradle on its back, feet up. Wait until reflexes have stopped.

6. Ring each hoof between hoof and dew claw with knife. Run point down back of each front leg. On rear legs run knife all the way up leg to rectum. Go just through the skin. As you begin to trim skin away, the dew claw becomes holding point.

7. Separate skin from pastern area. Jerk hide down to hock holding onto dew claws.

8. Now jerk up to crotch. Do both sides.

9. Separate tissue from severed line crotch. Leave scrotal or mammary tissue in hide. Separate flap of skin from rectum to leg.

10. Front end. Do same as far as knee. Jerk it to top of arm.

11. Draw knife across sternum from armpit to armpit. Go right under skin. Do not cut meat. At the point line crosses brisket, go from there to throat and open.

12. Begin working back the skin to the armpits.

13. Now you have skinned front end - exposing throat, front portion of each shoulder and at legs. Once you have separated hide off legs at the break joint, sever the foot from the leg. (The break joint is only present in animals under a year of age). Otherwise, remove foot at ball joint.

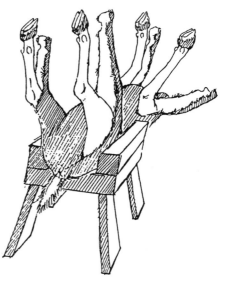

14. Take knife and open skin from sternum to crotch. In male remove penis.

15. Work hide back to side using fingers. Try to keep thin layer of muscle on the carcass. It is important to keep carcass intact. The entire stomach is now exposed.

16. Put in the hanging stick through hock between the Achilles tendon and lower section of thigh.

17. Suspend hanging stick from tree. Hoist animal off cradle so it is hanging.

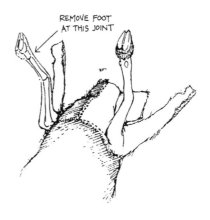

REMOVE FOOT AT THIS JOINT

Important: Rinse hands anytime you touch hide and then meat.

18. Cut from throat to sternum through sternum from middle of belly through throat. Chest cavity is exposed.

19. Work with fingertips and knife when necessary, working hide over rump. As you approach tail, grasp tail base and pull skin off.

20. At this point strip back with fingernails and knuckles trying to keep all muscle on carcass going right down backbone. Strip right off. Again, keep subcutaneous muscle attached to carcass and not hide. Pull off. Lay hide on rack.

21. Go to front. Wash carcass. Pour bucket of clean water over it.

22. Put in knife at crotch - blade side toward you. Put finger behind dull side of knife and push finger and knife down toward navel and eventually to sternum. Guts will fall forward.

23. Reach into the crotch and draw the rectum through pelvic arch.

24. Ring the rectum with knife. Tie it off. Reach into the crotch and draw the rectum through pelvic arch.

25. Pull bladder free and let this go with guts. Leave kidneys in kidney fat at back side of body.

26. Approaching thoracic cavity, spleen will be on left hand side. Pull loose - discard. At this point you will see liver on the right. Grab base of gall bladder and strip from liver, leaving liver in body cavity.

27. You will see bottom of esophagus. Tie this off. Cut this and guts will fall loose on the ground.

28. As you look at the kidneys and liver, you will see beneath them a distinct red and white line (Diaphram). This band separates the thoracic cavity from the abdominal cavity. Run knife along muscular strip (red and white line) and cut to sternum of each side. Grasp in center and pull away from muscle supporting liver. Do not take out.

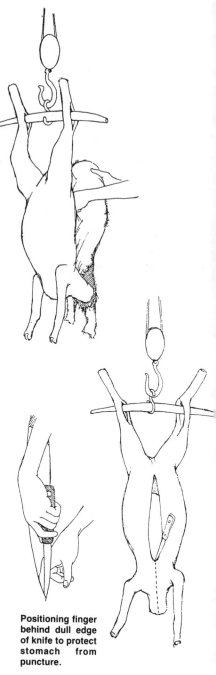

Positioning finger behind dull edge of knife to protect stomach from puncture.

29. Heart, lungs, windpipe and esophagus (pluck) will be in the material you are dragging away. Remove pluck, opening the throat the full length of the chest cavity.

30. Thoroughly wash carcass inside and out.

31. Remove tongue from head and any other parts of head you wish to use, such as brains, etc.

32. Keep the meat in a cool place or throw cold water on it periodically. If you are going to leave hanging for any length of time, wrap in a clean cloth.

33. Cut in desired pieces. Edible by-products would include liver, heart, tongue, kidneys, brains. If you have use for casings, for sausage, the small and large intestines could be salvaged.

34. All inedible visera should be buried or disposed of in a sanitary manner.

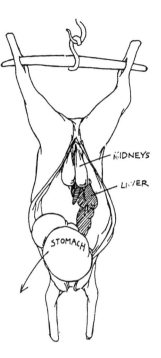

1. "Raising Goats for Milk and Meat", A Heifer Project International Training Course, Third Printing, July 1985. Rosalee Sinn.

2. Tri-County Goat Newsletter, University of California, Cooperative Extension, Tom Shultz, Dairy Farm Advisor.

3. Extension Goat Handbook, Fact Sheet A1, Page 2.

Section 19

Commerical Goat Products

XIX. COMMERCIAL GOAT PRODUCTS[1]

CREAM
If sold as such, an outlet is also needed for skim milk. Goat cream is pure white in color, and is colored yellow with annatto for commercial sale. The smaller fat globules make separation of the cream harder; the size of the globules also decreases as lactation advances. The cream rises so slowly that a small cream separator is useful.

BUTTER
A delicacy in Greece and Cyprus. Natural souring is usually satisfactory if one is careful and clean; otherwise, use a dairy butter starter.

CHEESE
The market is not large in this country (U.S.), but the demand is increasing. Cheese is cheaper and nutritionally superior to many meat protein sources. Cheese making is a very precise science, requiring careful control of acidity and temperature. The American Dairy Goat Association booklet has several recipes. Cheese has long been a practical way to store and market goat's milk when the herd is on an inaccessible mountain pasture.

CHEVON
This is goat meat. It tastes somewhat like lamb, mutton, and venison, but lacks the fat. Young kids are popular with some ethnic groups at Easter, and are slaughtered at 4 to 6 weeks of age. Castrated kids grow and taste better; descenting at least one month before slaughter is also recommended.

SKINS
Morocco leather is derived from long haired goats of cooler climates. Suede kid shoe leather comes from 9-18 month castrated and adult goats of warmer areas. True kid skins, from animals 1-6 months old, are used in a limited market for high class glove making. Dry kid skin weight, about 14 ounces, (396 gm.), hides from adult females weigh 1½-2 lbs, (700 to 900 gm), and those from adult males weight 3-5 lbs., (1.4 to 2.3 kg).

GOAT HAIR
Coarse hair is used for tent cloth, carpet and rug making. Mohair, from Angora goats, is mainly produced in the U.S., South Africa, and the eastern Mediterranean. Angora fleece develops poorly where annual rainfall exceeds 20 inches, (50 cm). Cashmere wool is the fluffy undercoat of goats living at high altitudes in the Himalayas. It is combed from the goat. The fleece is of poor quality in mild climates.

ANGORA GOATS

Smaller in size and weight than the dairy goat. They are raised to produce Mohair which yields a higher price than wool, especially from the older kids. Horns are left on this breed. They are white. The males, except those that are saved for bucks, are castrated at 8 to 10 months of age or earlier. Angora kids are weaned at about 3 months of age.

1. Material derived from *"Health Care of the Goat and Sheep"* R.A. Vanderhoof, VDM, 1987.

Section 20

Miscellaneous Medical, Surgical and Vaccination Information

XX. MISCELLANEOUS MEDICAL, SURGICAL AND VACCINATION INFORMATION[1]

1.. **Castration**. Castrates are known as wethers in both sheep and goats. Can be performed during the first week of life along with disbudding. Be sure to disinfect the area with Betadine (a tamed iodine solution) first. Be sure to inoculate with tetanus antitoxin.
Methods:
a) Elastration - Very widely practiced. There is danger of tetanus. This method is probably more painful and takes a longer time. It consists of applying a strong rubber band at the base of the testicles which is left there until the testicles fall away.

b) Knife or scalpel - regular surgery; probably the method preferred by most veterinarians. The lower third of the scrotum (sack) is cut off. Place pressure on the testicles above the cut area and force the testicles out of the cut end of the sack. Each testicle should then be grasped, pulled out as far as possible, and cut off. A sharp knife or scissors can be used for this process. Do not handle any tissue that remains in the goat as infection is very likely to occur.

An alternative method, after cutting off the scrotum, is to grasp the testicle and manually strip all attached tissue from it by holding the testicle in one hand, and pushing all skin and subcutaneous tissue upwards until the testicle is free. Then grasp the cord firmly above the testicle (wrap it around your fingers) and slowly pull downward until the cord breaks. Don't jerk, but pull slowly. Be sure to wash hands twice with soap and water, cleaning well under finger nails and drying with a clean towel, before handling tissue.

Young kids can be castrated without anesthia. Following castration, each kid should receive 500 to 750 (IU) of tetanus antitoxin (T.A.T.). If castration, disbudding, and de-scenting are done at the same time, only one dose of T.A.T. is necessary. An antibiotic powder may be applied to the scrotal area. If screwworms are a problem, always apply insecticide or a fly repellent to the wound. A sitting assistant can hold the kid firmly between his knees with the head down and the scrotal area exposed.

c) Burdizzo - probably the best method, as there is no external bleeding, so no fly attraction, but must be carefully and accurately performed. This is an instrument that pinches and crushes the spermatic cord and blood vessels leading to the testicles without breaking the skin. Do each side separately.

Mature bucks - must use anesthesia (putting to sleep) as goats are more subject to shock than other animals. An emasculator, (see glossary) should be used. Antibiotics should be given afterwards. Tetanus antitoxin is to be given if never inoculated for tetanus before.

If animal is to be used for meat, castrate before 2 months of age.

2. Dehorning and de-scenting. Older or mature animals. Horns are an important problem in goat herds. They are the most vicious of our domestic animals in relation to one another. They hurt and injure each other with their horns: they damage one another bad enough when they are dehorned.

A FORMULA FOR A GOOD ANTISEPTIC AND HEALING COMPOUND

Used for tail docking (removing portion of tail), castration, or any wound:

1 lb Nitrofurazone dressing (453.6 gm.) (a liquid)
1 lb. Sulfanilamide powder (453.6 gm.)
2 tablespoons wettable Co-Ral powder (25] - (½ ounce - 15 ml.)

Mix enough nitrofurazone solution to make a thick paste.

VACCINATION TECHNIQUES

Sterilizing Instruments, Syringes, and Needles

Clean instruments with soap and water after using and before sterilization. Scrub away all grease, blood, and tissue, then rinse with clean water. To sterilize, boil in clean water for 15 to 20 minutes. Cold sterilization involves soaking the clean instruments in Nolvasan or one of the quaternary ammonium disinfectants at the proper dilution and adequate time. Read label carefully. Soak instruments at least 60 minutes before using, but several hours would be better.

Do not use wet chemical sterilization for syringes and needles. Residue in the syringe and needle from the disinfectant can inactivate some vaccines. Boil syringes and needles instead.

INJECTION SITES

The following abbreviations are for corresponding type of injection and the site on the goat as described.

Intramuscular (IM) - injected deep within a major muscle mass, such as that in the hind leg or on the shoulder. It should be given with a 20, 19, 18 gauge, 2.5 to 4 cm (1 to 1½ inch) needle, pointed straight into the muscle. Before injecting the drug, always withdraw on the syringe plunger to make sure you have not hit a blood vessel. If this happens, blood will flow into the syringe. To correct, simply replace the needle in the muscle in a different site, and repeat procedure.

Subcutaneous (SC or SQ) - injected under the skin, usually in the neck or behind the shoulder. Usually a 1 to 2.5 cm (3/4 to 1 inch) needle is inserted at an angle through the skin. So that you do not stick yourself, pick up the skin with your fingers and insert the needle through the skin while it is pointed away from your fingers.

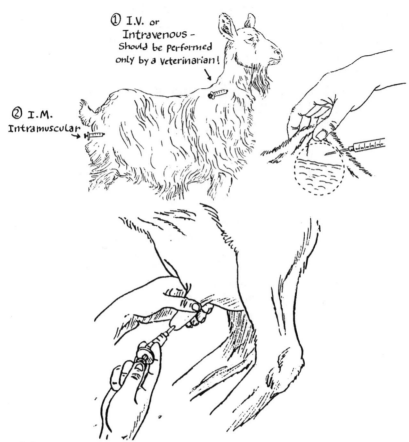

① I.V. or
Intravenous -
Should be performed
only by a veterinarian!

② I.M.
Intramuscular

Intravenous (IV) - injected into a vein, usually the jugular or neck vein as in the illustration. This procedure takes some skill and practice. Become thoroughly familiar with the method before attempting to use it. The vein must be blocked with one hand near the shoulder to enlarge it and make it visible. Usually a 4 cm, 18 gauge needle is used for IV injections. All IV injections should be given slowly, using only products specifically approved for this method.

Intrammary - injected within the milk gland, into the end of the teat through the natural opening. Always wash the teat end with soap and water and wipe it with alcohol or Betadine before injection. Use only sterile, blunt, teat infusion needles or "throw-away" mastitis medicine applicators. Unclean material entering the teat can cause mastitis.

SC or SQ = subcutaneous = under the skin
ID = intradermal = within the layers of the skin
IV = intravenous = into a vein
IP = intraperitoneal = into the abdomen cavity
IM = intramuscular = into a muscle

VACCINATION

1. Vaccine should be sterile and "in date" (not expired). Every time the needle punctures the rubber top of vaccine vial, bacteria are introduced into the vial.
2. Keep vaccine cold (refrigerated but not frozen) to reduce bacterial growth.
3. Best to use sterile needle for each animal. Or, at least, clean the needle by wiping with alcohol before each use. Some disease can be transmitted by "dirty" needles, e.g., anaplasmosis.
4. Give manufacturer's recommended dosage.
5. Restrain animal. A moving, struggling goat can cause tissue damage from a flaying needle.
6. Where to vaccinate. Vaccinations usually cause permanent swellings on goats, no matter where they are placed.

   a) Back (posterior) to scapula (shoulder blade). SC = subcutaneously (under the skin). Flatten out the swelling and rub in well to disperse the vaccine. Will still have a good chance of forming a swelling, at best.

   b) Be careful about vaccinating goats in the rump or rear leg region as you might strike a nerve or blood vessel, especially with very thin animals and kids.
7. Skin should be cleansed with Alcohol or Betadine before giving the injection.

EQUIPMENT AND PROCEDURES
FOR GIVING MEDICINE BY MOUTH

Drenching - Most goats will swallow liquids placed into the mouth if their head is held slightly upward. A dose syringe or bottle with a rubber hose attached will work well. If using dose syringe with a long nozzle or tube, be careful to place tube in the side of mouth -between teeth and facial wall. This will prevent the danger of forcing liquid down the windpipe into the lungs, causing pneumonia.

Place the end of the tube to the side of the tongue. Be careful not to injure the inside of the mouth.

Bolus or Pill Administration - A small balling gun is used to give pills or boluses to goats. The small guns are passed into the mouth over the hump on the tongue, and the plunger is gently pushed down taking care not to injure the mouth. Goats will often cough up boluses and they must be given again. Be patient. Do not overextend the head or the bolus may go down the windpipe. Apply a lubricant to the bolus before administering. It can be dipped into mineral oil or molasses for ease of swallowing. Pills can also be crushed and given in a small amount of tasty food, e.g. peanut butter.

In most cases, the appropriate dosage of medication for goats will be equivalent to that of sheep and/or pigs and will be printed on the label of the container.

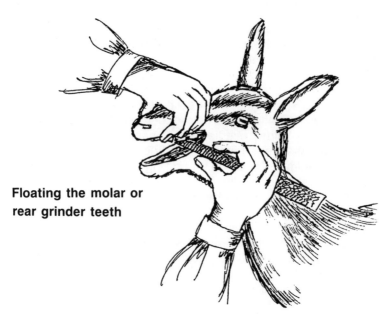

Floating the molar or rear grinder teeth

DENTAL

Examine mouth carefully with a flashlight. Look for grass awns or other foreign bodies. Look for abscessed teeth or sharp teeth cutting into the cheek. Floating (rasping or filing) the molars may be necessary occasionally, as with horses, if they start quidding (dropping chunks of food out of mouth) or salivating.

CULLING

It is vital to the overall productivity of the herd. Some goats will fall heir to "wasting disease" of which there is no treatment, and so should be eliminated. Examples of some causes: Johne's Disease, nerve problems, arthritis from CAE, etc.

ENVIRONMENTAL INSULTS

1. **Sunburn**. Light-skinned goats, like people, will often suffer when first turned out in the spring. Teats and udder can especially be damaged by sunburn. Prevention: Turn animals out into sunlight gradually and provide shade.

2. **Light sensitization**. Usually from 2 or 3 factors of which both or all must be present.

a) A white or unpigmented skin that is sensitive to ultraviolet rays.

b) Ingestion of certain plants that sensitizes the white skin to the damage by ulraviolet rays such as:

Saint-John's-wort
Alsike clover

c) Possibly a third factor: genetic predisposition (tendency) to the condition.

Photosensitization (sensitive to light): Edema (swelling) of lips, face, and ears is a common sign. Treatment: confine animal to barn or remove the offending plants.

3. **Frostbite**: Exposure of wet extremities to freezing. Newborn kids may have tips of their ears frozen, especially Nubians. Prevention/Treatment: tape ears up over head to improve blood circulation and prevent edema of the ear.

4. **Urine scald**: During breeding seasons, bucks will urinate on themselves, their legs and beard, etc. This often causes loss of hair. Treatment: hair should be clipped and skin washed with mild soap and then rinsed with sodium bicarbonate. Then coat the skin with petroleum jelly.

5. **Fly strike**: (maggot formation). From a wound or accumulated feces under the tail, that attracts flies to lay their eggs. Clean wounds and rectal area with hydrogen peroxide. Spray area with fly repellant.

6. **Predation**: Provide adequate protection from:
   a) Domestic large dogs running in packs.
   b) Wild carnivora, e.g., coyotes, bobcats, mountain lions.

1. Material derived from *"Health Care of the Goat and Sheep"*, R. A. Vanderhoof, VMD, 1987.

Section 21

Goat Raising In The Semi-Arid Tropics

Leucaena

XXI. GOAT RAISING IN THE SEMI-ARID TROPICS[1]

The term "semi-arid" describes restricted rainfall areas in warmer regions closer to the equator. Goat production is highly linked to the dry tropical conditions of the world.

Goat's feeding behavior is related directly to plant preference and plant part selectivity. The agility and dexterity combined with anatomical characteristics and distinctive rear limb articulations uniquely enable them to fit adequately to grazing conditions and respond satisfactorily when good quality pastures are used. The native vegetation in most areas seems to be adequate for meat and skin-type goats. However, it is known that this type of grazing is not adequate to sustain lactating dairy goats unless some sort of energy and protein supplement is made available. Tropical legumes have proved to be of great nutritive value for dairy goats.

LATERITE

In many tropical areas of the world, because of erosion and other factors, soil changes to aluminum and ferric hydroxide and becomes brick-hard and usually red. It contains very little organic matter where land is cleared for cash crops, after 2 to 3 years it tends to solidify upon exposure to air. This forms a brick-hard layer that is known as laterite. One promising solution to this problem could well be found in a plant known as Leucaena.

LEUCAENA

Providing protein-rich forage for cattle and goats is just one of the many uses of this so-called miracle plant, leucaena. Leucaena can also provide fire wood, timber, posts, raw material for pulp and paper, and many other products within a relatively short period of growth. It can do all this while improving the properties of soil such as laterite - increasing nitrogen content, loosening compacted soil and penetrating deep to bring nutrients to the surface. Its leaves are small and decompose rapidly to produce soil humus.

Leucaena leucocophala is one of ten species within the genus. It is called ipil-ipil in the Philippines, Kao Hoale in Hawaii and Iamtoro in Indonesia. A fast-growing tree, leucaena usually begins to function as a legume within 3 months of being planted. Like other legumes, it acquires the capacity to take its nitrogen supply from air when nitrogen-fixing bacteria rhizobia - in the soil infect its roots and form nodules. The resulting nitrogen compounds enrich the surrounding soil to the benefit of leucaena and any surrounding plants.

A problem exists however, with this plant. It is toxic to animals if their diet consists of 30 percent or more of leucaena. The function of the thyroid gland is impaired, resulting in goiter formation. If the ration is maintained at less than 30 percent leucaena, the rumen can detoxify the mimosine (toxic principle) and provide an excellent food supply relatively high in protein and calcium, similarly found in other leguminous feeds, e.g., alfalfa.

GOAT PRODUCTION AND MANAGEMENT IN BRAZIL
In the Sertao desert area of northeast Brazil:
1. Major problem: uncertain feed supply.
2. The primary product from the goat in northeast Brazil is meat production.
3. Goat milk and skins or hides are second.
   a) The size and the extent of defects in skins determine their value.
4. Although human food of animal origin is produced more efficiently through milk than through meat, relatively few goats are milked in Brazil.
5. One of the main problems in goat production is cost of fencing. Some have used solar powered electric fences.
6. Mixed rations for milking goats - Algaroba pods used as replacement for corn.

GOAT PRODUCTION IN SICHUAN PROVINCE, CHINA
Sichuan is one of the largest provinces in the People's Republic of China, situated in the southwestern part of the country on the upper reaches of the Yangtze River. The Chengdu Plain forms the Sichuan Basin. It has been known as the "land of Abundance," and has a population of 102 million people. Goats are an important "cash livestock" in Sichuan. By the end of 1985, there were 5.4 million goats that produced 24.3 million kg. of mutton and 3.7 million kg. of milk, annually. Goat hides have long been an important export resource of Sichuan Province.

There are six native breeds of goats in Sichuan and generally speaking have a medium-sized body, high production of mutton and hides, good reproductive performance, good adaptability and relatively low milk production.

European breeds were introduced in 1936, namely, Saanen, Toggenburg, and Nubian into Chengdu Province. Size, body weight, milk and meat production have increased as they were mixed in with the native goats. The dairy goat has become the main economic resource of the small farmer.

CHILE - GOAT IMPROVEMENT
The breeding of dairy goats started in Chile around 1555 with animals from Peru and later, Argentina. Intensive inbreeding produced low production of milk and meat. From 1930 to 1955, several importations of European breeds such as Nubian and Saanen were made, dispersing these breeds throughout the country. The Saanen goat better resists the cold conditions of the South of Chile.

As these European breeds are mixed in with the native goats, tolerance to local climate and feeding conditions will be developed. The goal is to improve size, milk, milk fat, and meat production while maintaining resistance to local conditions.

GOAT PRODUCTION FOR SMALL HOLDERS IN SOUTH INDIA

The Goat population of India grew from 47 million in 1951 to over 71 million today, with a 43 percent turnover (278,000 tons of meat) for consumption.

Landless peasants can raise several goats, feeding them grasses and legumes from roadsides.

Milk and meat production from goats often represents a significant improvement in nutrition and income for landless people.

Constraints to goat production for these farmers include climatic problems, infertility, disease, access to land and feed, and lack of understanding appropriate husbandry practices.

Goat milk is primarily consumed by the farmer's family but some is sold. Prices are based on fat tests.

Goats are providing nutrition and income to small farmers throughout India.

GOAT MEAT PRODUCTION IN FIJI

Feed is readily available in Fiji, with grass pastures able to maintain three to four goats per acre. There is also a good supply of coconut meal, maize, sorghum, broom corn seed, wild tapioca, rice straw and molasses.

Major debilitating diseases have not so far occurred. Important restrictions regarding health are strict. The primary concern of producers is that of internal parasites.

GOAT PRODUCTION IN HONDURAS

The health and nutrition status of children has been substantially improved by the introduction of goats to families. It has been determined that, under the prevailing conditions, goats do not impose additional constraints to the rural family. The major drawbacks of these projects is the lack of "outside" bucks, causing a degree of inbreeding. To avoid such problems, three breeding centers have been implemented, with either Anglo-Nubian, French Alpine or Saanen bucks.

GOAT PRODUCTION IN HAITI

Fifty percent of the land is too steep, too dry, and too rocky for cultivation, however, it is suitable for a wide variety of grains and legumes, and for reforestation. Leucaena - a nitrogen fixing legume - would provide excellent feed for goats and at the same time help restore a more fertile soil.

Increased production of meat and milk from goats would directly benefit the nutritional status of Haitians. Both protein and calories are in short supply.

The malnutrition of children under five years of age is extremely high. Haiti has the lowest per capita supply of animal protein compared to Central and South American countries - only 7.1 grams per day. It has been shown that a few ounces of milk each day will improve the well being and nutritional status of children.

Loose herding and tethering are the predominant goat production systems in Haiti. In the loose herding system, the animals roam about uncontrolled in rural and urban areas, subsisting on whatever feed and/or food refuse they can find. A large majority of goats in Haiti are kept under the loose herding system. Tethering - tying the animal with a 10 to 12 foot rope and moving its location when the surrounding feed is exhausted - is more common in areas where row crops or gardens are planted. It is doubtful that under either production system the goats can fulfill their nutrient requirements; particularly in a situation such as Haiti.

PROBLEMS IN RAISING GOATS IN KENYA

1. Insufficient amounts of adequate quality feed on a year round basis. On small farms, the demand for human food crops takes priority over production of feed of livestock.

2. Tick-borne diseases, such as anaplasmosis, trypanosomiasis, heartwater. Control measures: dipping or spraying - not commonly practiced because of cost and lack of assistance.

3. The need for more time for the animals to forage and graze; also milking animals need more access to drinking water.

4. Socioeconomic constraints: many would rather produce goats for status symbol - for capital storage - and secondarily for production.

5. Lack of status in keeping goats - instead of cattle, a higher status symbol.

**GOAT PRODUCTION IN THE
PHILIPPINES**

Goats are provided with good roughage in the feeders every day. Rotation grazing is also practiced to control internal parasites and to be able to maintain more animals per hectare.

Napier grass and ipil-ipil (50:50) are used as "cut and carry" roughage (ipil-ipil is the native Philippine name for the leucaena plant). Rice straw, corn, and sorghum silage are also used for feeding.

1, 2, 3. From personal correspondence and conversion with Floyd Votaw, DMV, Lt. Col. retired, who has spent much time in Haiti and the Philippines.

GLOSSARY

A

Abomasum - The fourth of the four stomachs of the ruminant animal. It is the true stomach and is similar in conformation to that of man.

Abscess - A localized collection of pus in the tissues of the body, often accompanied by swelling and inflammation, and generally caused by bacteria.

Acetonemia - Increased amount of acetone in the blood.

Acute - Sharp, severe having a rapid onset.

Aerosol - Producing a fine spray.

Anemia - Abnormally low number of red cells in blood.

Anorexia - A diminished or complete lack of appetite.

Anterior - The front or toward the head.

Anthelmintic - A remedy for destruction of intestinal worms.

Antibiotics - A chemical agent produced by a microorganism which has the capacity to inhibit the growth of, or to kill other microorganisms.

Antitoxin - A substance that counteracts a toxin or poison.

Arthropods - The biological classification of spiders and mites.

Articular - Pertaining to a joint.

Aseptic - Free from disease-forming bacteria or viruses.

Aspirated - Drawn or sucked up, like in a syringe.

Ataxia - Lack of coordination in walking or moving. Animal acts like it is drunk.

Awns - The slender bristles that form a spikelet in some cereal plants and grasses.

Azimycin - A proprietary compound consisting of penicillin, streptomycin, antihistamine and a corticosteroid. Injectable for infections. Not advisable for pregnant animals.

B

Bacteria - Microscopic one cell plant life that can invade the body tissue and blood and multiply, causing disease. There are, however, beneficial bacteria.

Bacterin - A vaccine consisting of the killed bacteria that is the cause of a particular disease. A booster inoculation should be given at a specified time, usually 1 to 2 months later.

Ballottment - A forceful, rapid pushing into the side of abdomen of a pregnant animal with the fist to attempt to feel a fetus.

Benign - Favorable; not dangerous, e.g., a benign tumor.

Betadine - A tamed iodine preparation. Very widely used because of excellent antiseptic qualities.

B.I.D. - Twice a day.

Biologicals - Preparations made from living organisms and their products, including serums, vaccines, bacterins, antigens, and antitoxins.

Blepharospasm - Twitching and/or closing of the eyelid.

Bloat - The rumen is abnormally inflated with air or gas. Also stomach and intestines sometimes.

Bottle jaw - Soft swelling of tissue under the jaw and neck of animals, usually as a result of a heavy worm infestation.

Browse - Refers to eating herb type plants, e.g., brush and tree leaves.

Burdizzo - A large plier-like instrument used for bloodless castration.

C

Caprine - Goat

Carbohydrate - The starches, sugars, and cellulose.

Cardiac - Refers to the heart.

Carpal - The "knee" joint in animals. Corresponds to the wrist joint in humans.

Caseous - Thickened; cheese-like.

Castration - Removal of the testicles in the male.

Cercariae - Formative stage of liver fluke. Also see Miracidia.

Cervix - The neck and opening of the uterus. The term cervical area also refers to the neck - between head and shoulders.

Cestodes - Tapeworms.

Chevon - Meat from the goat.

Chlorhexidine - An antiseptic.

Choke - An obstruction that lodges in the esophagus, like an apple, orange or potato.

Chronic - A disease that has become long-standing.

Clinical - The manifestation of disease in the living animal. The disease that can be easily seen.

CNS - Central nervous system, consisting of the brain, brain stem and spinal column.

Coccidiocidal - Refers to killing coccidia.

Coccidiostat - A preparation that inhibits the growth and reproduction of coccidia, but does not kill them.

Colostrum - The first milk of the mother after she gives birth. It is thicker and more yellow than regular milk and lasts only a few days.

Congenital - Refers to a condition that developed before birth and in the uterus.

Conjunctivitis - Inflammation of the lining around the eyeball and inside the eyelid.

Copper sulfate - $CuSo_4$, a chemical sometimes used in foot baths in about a 10 percent solution.

Cornea - The outer layer of the eye that is clear.

Coronary band - The top portion of the foot from which new hoof material grows.

Cotyledons - The many rather large red structures on the uterine wall that are attached to the placenta or afterbirth and serve in the interchange of nutrients from the mother to the fetus.

Creep feed - A method whereby the young can "creep" into a small space in an enclosure and eat without interference from the mother.

Cud - The small eructated mass of rumen contents that is chewed and then swallowed, which then passes into the reticulum or second stomach. This is the process known as rumination.

Cyanosis - Tissues turning blue from a lack of oxygen.

D

Defecation - The act of voiding feces.

Dehydration - A diminishing of the normal moisture or water in the body tissue.

Dexamethasone - A corticosteroid.

Docking - Removing usually a portion of the tail by one of several methods.

Dorsal - The top or toward the spinal column of an animal.

Drenching - Giving a liquid by mouth.

Duodenum - The first third of the small intestine.

Dystocia - Difficult or abnormal birth.

Dyspnea - Difficult breathing.

E

Edema - Swelling of tissue by fluid retention in the tissue.

Elastration - Castration or tail-docking by use of rubber bands.

Electrolyte - A solution containing chemicals such as potassium, magnesium, phosphorus, calcium and others that are essential to maintain hydration of the animal body. These become depleted during vomiting, hemorrhaging and/or diarrhea and can cause dehydration, often severe and dangerous.

Emasculators - A scissor-like instrument used for castration that crushes and cuts simultaneously.

Endemic - A disease peculiar to a certain region or animals and occurs more or less constantly in a locality. Often sporadic.

Enterotoxemia - Toxins in the blood originating from the intestines. Term usually refers to the specific disease: overeating disease, caused by **Clostridium perfringens** type C and D.

Enzyme - A protein capable of accelerating or producing by catalytic action a specific change in the body.

Exotoxin - A toxin produced outside the body.

F
Febrile - Having a temperature above normal.

Fecal flotation test - A procedure where feces is diluted with a special solution which causes intestinal worm eggs to float to the surface so they can be examined with a microscope.

Feces - Intestinal excrement, manure.

Feral - Wild, untamed animal. Usually a domesticated animal(s) that has turned wild.

Floating - rasping or filing the molar or rear grinding teeth to remove sharp, projecting points that may be cutting into the inner cheek.

Flushing - Gradually increasing the level of nutrition of a breeding doe three weeks prior to mating to promote multiple births.

G
Gangrene - Necrosis or dying of any tissue.

Genitalia - All of the external organs of reproduction of either sex.

Gestation - The span of time from conception to birth.

GI tract - Gastrointestinal tract.

Graze - Eating grasses and clovers.

H
Haemonchosis - A condition of having a great and possibly harmful number of stomach worm infestation.

HCN - Hydrocyanic acid. Same as prussic acid.

Head-press - A morbid state where animal stands with head pressing against a wall.

Hectare - Land measurement equalling 2.47 acres.

Hemorrhagic - An accumulation of blood in or from any tissue.

Hock - The next joint higher up from the fetlock or "ankle" of rear leg. It contains the tarsal bones.

Hormone - A chemical substance produced in the body by an organ, which has a specific regulatory effect on the activity of another organ.

Hydrogen peroxide - A liquid chemical (H_2O_2) that serves as an excellent disinfectant on wounds.

Hydrometria - Water in the uterus.

I

ID - Intradermal; within the layers of the skin.

IM - Intramuscular; into a muscle.

M

Merozite - One of the stages of the developing coccidia.

Metabolism - The chemical process of absorbing food.

Metacarpus - Front leg. The bones distal or below the carpus (wrist in humans) and the "knee" in animals.

Metatarsal - Back leg. The bones distal or below the tarsus (ankle in humans) and the hock in animals.)

Mg - Milligrams 1/1000th of a gram.

Miracidia - Formative stage of liver fluke. Also see Cercariae.

Mite - A tiny (microscopic) creature that lives within the skin and causes mange. It is contagious.

Ml - Milliliter. 1/1000 of a liter. This is the same as cc.

Mucous membrane - The inner lining of the mouth and other body cavities that produce mucus.

N

Nanny - A doe. A mothering goat.

Necropsy - Postmortem operation. Autopsy.

Necrosis - The dying of a tissue or organ.

Neonate - A newly born animal.

Nictitans - The "third eyelid" that reflects over the eyeball.

Nits - Lice eggs attached to the hair or juvenile lice not fully formed.

Nodules - A small node which is solid and can be detected by touch.

O

Oestrus ovis - The nasal fly larva, primarily of sheep but occasionally in goats.

Omasum - The third of the four stomachs of ruminants. Also called manyplies.

Opacity - Opaqueness or cloudiness, usually used in reference to the impaired cornea of the eye.

Opisthotonus - A spasm condition in which the animal's head is thrown back and feet are stretched out straight. It occurs in tetanus.

Orifice - An opening, an entrance to a cavity or tube.

Ovine - Sheep.

P

Palpated - To detect symptoms of a disease, e.g., a swelling, by hand exploration.

Papules - Pimples. Small skin swellings.

Pen-strep - An abbreviation for penicillin-streptomycin.

Perineum - The area between and including the rectum and the external genitalia.

Peroxide - A chemical with a high oxygen content. Sometimes used as an abbreviation for hydrogen peroxide.

Pinch Test - A preliminary or screening test indicative of dehydration. Thin skin like around the face is pinched into a ridge and the length of time that the skin holds this formation before returning to its flattened normal state is roughly indicative of the degree of animal's dehydration.

Placenta - The membranes that surround the developing embryo and fetus. The "afterbirth."

Placentitis - Inflammation of the placenta or afterbirth membranes.

Polyarthritis - Inflammation of several joints together.

Polygastric - More than one stomach.

Posterior - Toward the rear.

PPM - Parts per million.

Predation- One animal preying upon another.

Prognosis - A forecast as to the probable outcome of a disease. The prospect as to the recovery from a disease as indicated by the nature and symptoms of the case.

Propylene glycol - A clear, colorless, nearly odorless, viscous liquid which has a slight characteristic sweetish taste. It is used in treating animals for acetonemia (ketosis).

Pruritis - Itching.

Pseudocyesis - Pseudopregnancy, false pregnancy.

Pulmonary - Pertaining to the lungs.

Purulent - Full of, forming, or discharging pus.

Pustules - Small, pus-filled pimples.

Q

Q.I.D. - Four times per day.

Quaternary ammonium compound - A very efficient disinfecting agent. It is usually supplied in a concentrated liquid and is diluted for use.

Quidding - Dropping chewed or unchewed food or quids out of the mouth.

R

Radius - One of the long bones (its companion is the ulna) in the forearm of man and just above the knee in the front legs of animals.

Reticulum - The second of the four stomachs of ruminants.

Rudimentary - An undeveloped or underdeveloped state.

Rumen - The first of the four stomachs of ruminant animals. It is the largest of the four. The paunch.

Ruminant - The class of animals that have four stomachs and ruminate (chew their cud).

S

SC or SQ - Subcutaneous; under the skin.

Scapula - The shoulder blade bone.

Scours - Diarrhea.

Scrotum - The pouch which contains the testicles.

Sebaceous glands - Are located in the skin and secrete a greasy lubricating substance, sebum.

Septicemia - Bacteria or virus in the blood stream.

Shedder - An animal that has a bacterial, viral, or parasitic disease, often non-clinical, (not evident) that sheds or disseminates the infection to other individuals or to a herd.

S.I.D. - Once per day.

Sodium iodide solution - Contains usually 20 percent sodium iodide in saline solution. It is given IV for certain diseases.

Somatic cells (in milk) - Cells other than the white blood cells. Usually consist of epithelial cells from the inner lining of the mammary gland or udder.

Spermatazoa - The mature male reproductive or germ cell which serves to impregnate the ovum of the female.

Spermatogenesis - The process of the production of spermatazoa.

Spores - The seed-like structures that many bacteria can convert to when outside the body. They are usually viable for varying lengths of time, and have the capacity to change back into the vegetative form if they regain entrance to the body. A good example is the anthrax bacillus.

SQ - See SC.

Sternum - The breast bone.

Steroids - A group name for compounds that are naturally formed or synthetically produced hormones. such as progesterone, adrenocortical hormones, gonadal hormones, etc.

Stethoscope - An instrument for listening to heart and lung sounds and any other part of the body.

Stifle - The true knee joint of animals. The next higher joint from the hock - rear leg.

Supernumerary teats - Extra teats on an udder, usually rudimentary and non-functional.

T

Tail docking - Cutting off a portion of the tail.

TDN - Total digestible nutrients.

Tetanus antitoxin - Is a serum that confers immediate immunity but only lasts about 2 weeks.

Tetanus toxoid - A killed vaccine which causes a buildup of immunity after about 9 days and lasts for about a year.

Tetracycline hydrochloride - An antibiotic.

THCl - An abbreviation for tetracycline hydrochloride, an antibiotic.

Tibia - One of the long bones in the rear leg between the stifle and the hock.

T.I.D. - Three times per day.

Toxin - Poison.

Toxoid - A type of vaccine that stimulates the production of antitoxin in the body.

Trocar - An instrument composed of a sharp, pointed rod extending down through a sheath or canula. It is used to relieve bloat by letting gas escape when inserted into the rumen from the left flank. After the instrument is placed into the rumen, the pointed rod is removed while the canula portion remains in place in the rumen.

U

Ulna - One of the long bones (its companion is the radius) in the forearm of man and just above the knee in the front legs of animals.

Umbilicus - The navel.

Urethra - The tube structure that carries urine from the bladder down to the outside. It also serves as a channel for the semen in the male.

V

Vagina - The opening in the female extending from the vulva to the uterine cervix.

Vas deferrens - The two long tubules that carry the sperm from the testicles to the urethra.

Ventral - The underside, or that portion of the anatomy closest to the ground.

Vermifuge - A material or compound for treating internal parasites.

Vulva - The external genital organ of the female.

W

Wattles - Skin appendages hanging down from the neck on some goats.

Wether - A castrated male sheep or goat.

XYZ

Xeropthalmia - Excessive dryness of the eyes leading to corneal ulceration and an invitation to bacterial infection. Usually caused by a lack of vitamin A in the diet.

BIBLIOGRAPHY

Extension Goat Handbook - Extension Service.
United States Department of Agriculture:
Washington, D.C.
G. Haenlein and D. Ace, editors. 1984.
Guss, Samuel B.

Management and Diseases of Dairy Goats"
Dairy Goat Journal Publishing Corp.
Scottsdale, AZ, 1977.

The IDR Reports, Voc. 12, No. 4, January 1984.

IV International Conference on Goats
Brasilia, Brazil, March 1987
Heifer Project International, Inc.
Little Rock, Arkansas

The Merck Veterinary Manual, 6th Edition and 7th Edition
Clarence M. Fraser, ed.
Merck and Co., Inc.
Rahway, N.J.

Notes and Personal Communication from Dr. Floyd Votaw DVM,
Lt. Co. (Ret.)
Fullerton, CA

Goat Health Handbook
Thedford, T. R.
Winrock International
Morrilton, Arkansas

"Raising Goats for Milk and Meat", a Heifer International Training
Course, third printing, July 1985, Rosalee Sinn

University of California, Davis
Nancy E. East, DVM, Professor of Small Ruminant Medicine

Goat and Sheep Production in the Tropics
C. Devendra and G.B. McLeroy
(Longman-London and New York)
Health Care of the Goat and Sheep
R.A. Vanderhoof, VMD, Woodlake, California, 1987.

Your Dairy Goat, A Western Regional Extension Publication
Revised July 1981, WREP −47

Veterinary Pharmaceuticals and Biologicals, 6th Edition, 1989-1990.
Veterinary Medicine Publishing Co., Lenexa, Kansas 66215